A Doctor's Calling:
A Matter of Conscience

Hazel J. Magnussen

Wembley Publishing

Library and Archives Canada Cataloguing in Publication

Magnussen, Hazel J., 1943-
A doctor's calling : a matter of conscience / Hazel J. Magnussen.

Includes bibliographical references.
ISBN 0-9739843-0-9

1. Snider, Douglas G. (Douglas George) 2. Murder--Alberta--Fairview.
3. Cooper, Abraham. 4. Medical care--Alberta--Fairview. 5. Criminal justice,
Administration of--Alberta. 6. Physicians--Alberta--Biography. I. Title.

HV6535.C33F33 2006   364.152'3'0971231   C2005-907832-4

Published by Wembley Publishing
            Parksville, BC
            E-mail: doctorscalling@shaw.ca

Cover Photo: Dunvegan Bridge over Peace River near Fairview, Alberta,
            by Don Pettit, Peace photoGraphics Inc.

Printed in Canada

This book is dedicated to the memory of
my brother,
Dr. Douglas George (Schattschneider) Snider
and our parents,
George and Sophie Schattschneider

*We must have the will power to sail
in whatever course our conscience indicates.*

*Douglas Schattschneider
Valedictorian Address
Salisbury High School, Class 1957*

Table of Contents

Foreword

Hazel Magnussen's account of her brother's life and death deals with many facets of human dynamics. I was impressed with both the detailed information and Magnussen's insightful observations drawn from her family's painful experience.

From my experience in professional regulation, I was most struck by the powerful messages this book conveys about disruptive physician behavior. The medical profession has long recognized the risks associated with chemically impaired physicians and has developed effective interventions to mitigate those risks. However, until very recently, we have failed to acknowledge the destructive potential of unchecked physician behavior and have failed to develop effective interventions.

Hazel Magnussen has done the medical profession an enormous service by challenging the profession to critically revisit the history surrounding her brother's murder by a medical colleague. We are challenged to ask what can and should be done to identify and modify destructive physician behavior at an earlier stage. I would encourage all persons involved in medical management to read this book.

Dr. Dennis A. Kendel, MD
Registrar
College of Physicians and Surgeons of Saskatchewan

Preface

This book chronicles the life and career of country doctor Douglas George Snider, and his efforts to resolve an issue affecting health care in his community in the Alberta Peace Peace River region. Ultimately, his life was taken in the line of duty. The fact that it happened in a small western Canadian town demonstrates that malicious disruption, allowed to fester, can wreak its havoc anywhere.

The physician who was killed was my brother. In our last conversation a few days before his death, we talked about his impending semi-retirement and his desire to write about his life and work as a country doctor. Soon after his death, I resolved to write that book for him.

I would rather not have to include the traumatic events leading up to and following his death, but sadly, they are now part of the story. Important parts of that history were ruled inadmissible in the trial of the man who was charged with Doug's murder and later convicted of manslaughter. When the defendant and his lawyer concocted a bizarre, fictitious tale about Doug's desire to disappear; the need to document the truth about the complex series of events became especially urgent.

My brother and I shared a passion for our work in health care, and knew that taking a stand for what we believed came at a cost. In the end, Doug paid with his life. In my search for meaning and hope in this tragedy, I am compelled to defend my brother's honor and advocate for reform in the two social systems that play integral roles in this account – the medical regulatory and the criminal justice systems.

Although the story has received wide media coverage, a full report of the events leading up to the crime has yet to be told publicly. This book draws heavily on official documents, news reports, notes of legal proceedings, academic research and my personal experience and reflections.

Unfortunately, the offender has not revealed the mystery of all that happened during and after his meeting with Doug on the night of the crime. He continues to defy authorities and threatens to get even with those he sees as a threat. I sincerely regret that Abe is unwilling to take responsibility for his actions.

No matter where it occurs, violence and crime shatters trust and the well being of individuals and entire communities. I hope that the telling of this story will inform, and inspire positive change and healing in a society where intimidation, bullying and violence are all too common.

Hazel J. (Schattschneider) Magnussen

Acknowledgements

To my husband, Lloyd, who has patiently provided both moral and computer support throughout this six-year project.

To members of my family, who trusted and encouraged me to write a story that belongs to all of us.

To those who reviewed the manuscript, especially Dr. Dennis Kendel who wrote the foreword and to David Staples and Rev. Foster Freed whose comments appear on the back cover.

Part One

The Doctor Responds
to an Evening Phone Call

Twilight and evening bell,
And after that the dark!
And may there be no sadness or farewell,
When I embark;
For tho' from out our bourne of time and place
The flood may bear me far,
I hope to see my Pilot face to face
When I have crossed the bar."
Alfred Lord Tennyson[1]

---

[1] Doug included this poem in his high school yearbook that he edited.

Chapter One

In the quiet Alberta town of Fairview, the heart of the rolling hills and fields of the Peace River country, a mystery was about to unfold. It was a few minutes before 9 p.m. on May 5, 1999, the eve of Doug's sixtieth birthday, when he received a phone call from another local doctor.

Neither Doug nor his wife, Jean, could possibly have known that after that call, nothing would ever be the same again for them, their family, friends, or the agricultural community that had been their home for thirty years. The call had been brief, but the pensive physician thought the conversation might finally lead to a long-awaited breakthrough towards some kind of peace declaration at last.

Jean had gone to bed earlier than usual that evening because she was feeling slightly under the weather. As she lay there, the call seemed just like all those countless others that had come in over the thirty years of Doug's medical practice.

Down the hall, the receiver replaced, Doug stood thinking for another moment or two. And as the devout doctor processed what had been said during the call, he became convinced that this was the opportunity for which he had prayed for years. Dr. Abe Cooper had called to invite Doug to a meeting at his clinic at 9:15 p.m. Abraham Cooper, or 'Abe' as he was known to friends in and around Fairview, finally wanted to talk.

Doug looked at his watch. That was only minutes away. He had preparations to make. The unexpected contact from Cooper had come at a time when much of Doug's own thinking was directed to his planned retirement. It would be more like semi-retirement, only months ahead, a partial withdrawal at least from the profession that he loved and to which he had dedicated himself many years before.

Perhaps, after all, he would be able to move on gracefully, with the dignity befitting his career of devotion and position, with all the loose ends satisfactorily and neatly tied up. Doug walked from the kitchen to the room where Jean lay. There was no hiding the excitement in his voice. "Abe wants to talk," he told her.

Jean sighed at yet another mention of the man that, in the most recent of the thirty years her husband had spent in medical practice, had come to haunt their family, their work, their home and everyday existence. Doug broke a family rule when he told her who had called.

The years-long acrimony between the doctors had deteriorated to the stage where Jean had asked Doug not to even mention either the other physician or the tiresome conflict. For too long, Abe Cooper had been Doug's nemesis, and, conversely, Abe had too long numbered Doug amongst his.

Doug left the bedroom and continued preparing to keep his appointment a few minutes' walk along the neat avenue running due west from his home in the north end of town. He must have been thinking about the tempestuous dealings with Abe since the latter's arrival in town. Doug was likely especially optimistic that evening because he had overheard that the hospital staff was planning a surprise birthday party for him the next day.

Doug had not sought power, but after many years in the area, had gained prominence and respect. At six feet two and 200 pounds, he was an imposing but gentle man, soft-spoken, committed, decisive and rooted deeply in his family, in his career, and in his faith. He was to a large degree the epitome of a country doctor.

Most folk in Fairview considered him to be a man who really cared. Many of them were well aware that five years earlier he had had to overcome his own personal demons, alcoholism and dependence on valium, to continue being able to function among them. Perhaps as a result, they reasoned that their doctor's success in dealing with his own problems had added to his arsenal of empathy and capacity to look after them.

True, through the years, there had been some conflict involving the small medical community in the town. But on the whole, knowledge of the real gravity of a situation ultimately destined for calamity had remained within that very small section of the community.

Some people in town reckoned the conflicts that manifested themselves occasionally on the letters page of the local *Fairview Post* newspaper, would have been typical in any small North American town where several physicians operated in such close proximity to each other. And wouldn't the same dynamic also have applied to lawyers, journalists, or accountants? Probably.

* * *

Abe Cooper came to Fairview in 1989. As men and doctors, Doug and Abe could not have been more different. They were at variance in health care philosophy and values, their working demeanors were direct contradictions, and their personalities were at opposite ends of the human spectrum.

Doug was a home lover, a cyclist, a reader and a hobby art collector. Abe, a private pilot with a black belt in martial arts and a competitive zest for badminton, approached life aggressively, seemed abrasive, and to more than a few, downright arrogant.

The staff at the hospital really didn't take to Dr. Cooper pretty much from the start. No matter, those in the community who became his patients seemed to grow accustomed to the gruffness, took to liking him, and came to fiercely swear by his efficiency and competence.

In those early days, there were sincere efforts by the two doctors to get along. In October 1992, for example, Abe and his wife, Fay, had dinner with Doug and Jean, office nurse Vi Landry and her husband Ken, during a joint Snider-Landry working holiday in Las Vegas. Doug and Abe were both attending a medical conference called "Primary Care Update". The Coopers had flown to the conference in their private plane.

That evening at least, there was no sign of any ill will at the little Canadian gathering amid the American glitz and glitter far to the south. Doug picked up the dinner tab.

But later, back in Fairview, back in their working environment, it became more and more inevitable that before too much more time was to pass, Abe and the rest of the community's medical establishment would clash.

There were reports of Abe having rows with hospital staff and fellow doctors, of complaints from nurses of his bullying attitude and apparent lack of respect for the job they did. The situation deteriorated and eventually resulted in Abe's loss of hospital admitting privileges.

Seemingly in retaliation, Abe Cooper filed a $3.2 million lawsuit against Doug and two other doctors for their part in what he claimed was a deliberate conspiracy to ruin his reputation and run him out of Fairview. There were those in town who claimed to have become physically afraid of the strapping, boisterous, 60-year-old Cooper. Others feared being sued by him. For others it seemed simply best not to become involved, to remain silent.

* * *

Now, out of the blue, in the evening of what had been a thoroughly good day for Doug, Abe's call had brought some reason for optimism that an end to the endless nightmare might be in sight. Doug must have felt there was finally hope of a peaceful settling of differences and the stressful matter of the lawsuit that had long hung over the health care community, like an ominous prairie thunderhead that simply refused to move on.

He walked from the living room to the kitchen and opened a cupboard. From it, he took several sheets of letter-sized, letterhead stationery bearing his name, folded them neatly, and clutched them in his hand. He figured notes might have to be taken or perhaps something might have to be put in writing. He was just about to go through the front door a few stairs down from the kitchen when Jean walked out of their bedroom. She was surprised he was still there until he explained his meeting with Cooper was not until 9:15 p.m.

She had been thinking about the implications of the telephone call too. With the contentious issue of the restoration of Abe's hospital privileges in mind, she asked Doug, "Why don't you go along with it? You are retiring."

Principled as ever and with no hint of capitulation, complete or minimal, he told her: "There's got to be rules."

Almost as an afterthought, Jean, referring to Abe's clinic, said: "Maybe he wants to sell his building." They were the last words she ever spoke to Doug.

He didn't reply. Instead, at 9:10 p.m., May 5, 1999, he turned and opened the front door. He closed it gently behind him and, through a speck or two of starting rain, strolled hopefully, even optimistically, to face his destiny.

Chapter Two

During the overnight hours leading into the day that was her husband's birthday, Jean awoke from a fitful sleep and found herself to be alone. She realized Doug's side of the bed was undisturbed, the sheets and the pillow unruffled. She got up, explored, and discovered he wasn't anywhere else in the house either.

It was about 1:50 a.m. on May 6. She looked out of the front window and saw that both the family vehicles, a truck and a car, were still parked in the driveway. He must have walked, she thought sleepily, somewhat surprised.

Her head clearing, and now growing slightly anxious, she put on her robe and left the house on the northeastern fringe of the town. She slid into the family's blue-green Chrysler Intrepid, turned the ignition key, slipped the car into gear, backed out, and set off west along the generously treed avenue towards the main street a short distance away.

When she reached the intersection, she hung a left and cruised slowly south down the wide boulevard, deserted apart from a few cars and pickup trucks angle-parked along the curbs bordering its sidewalks. As she drove south, the town's huge grain elevator just to the left of the distant end of the street was starkly highlighted by the orange glow of the streetlights.

The wipers ticked back and forth across the sloping windshield, and she peered to her right through what was by then a light, steady drizzle. Her attention became fixed on a square, white, flat-roofed, single-storey building set back a few feet from the western side of the street just behind a rough patch of semi-tended grass trying ever so hard to pass as cultivated lawn.

It was about two hundred steps away from the hospital that had been both the scene of, and the focus of, many of the clashes between Doug, his ally associates, and Abe over the years. The inconsequential little structure housed Abe Cooper's clinic and the glass front door bore his capital-lettered black-type monogram to make the point.

The lights are still on, she thought, creeping past the front of the building and squinting out over the car's vacant right-hand passenger seat and through its side window. They must still be talking.

She drove home, not totally unconcerned, but not unduly worried either. After all, Doug and Abe would have had a lot of history to cover if, finally, there was to be anything resembling conciliation between them.

By 2:30 a.m., though, her anxiety level was definitely rising, and she called both the Fairview Hospital and the Grande Prairie Hospital, an hour away to the south in the city of the same name, to see if her husband might for some reason have moved on after his meeting. He had not been seen at either facility.

Again she waited.

At 5:30 a.m., unable to contain her worry or curiosity any longer, she again got into the Intrepid and retraced her route past Cooper's office. The lights were still on. This time she thought of getting out and knocking at the front door, but decided against it, and returned once more to her empty home.

For two hours she worked the telephone trying to locate her beloved husband, calling the hospitals again, his office in the mall halfway down the main street, his office nurse, even hotels and motels. It was unusual for him not to call, day or night, when he was away.

At one point, hospital night staff thinking that Doug must surely have returned by that time, phoned his home to obtain an insulin order for a patient. They were alarmed when they heard that there was still "no news of Dr. Snider."

By 7:30 a.m., Jean had exhausted both herself and all of her options. There was only one more call left to make. She picked up the telephone one last time and dialed the number of the local detachment of the Royal Canadian Mounted Police.

Snider home in Fairview.

Chapter Three

Most police services in Canada apply an unwritten rule not to act directly upon a 'missing person' report for at least 48 hours after receiving it. Experience has shown them and other law agencies across the globe there's usually a simple explanation for such so-called disappearances. The supposed victim or missing person usually turns up well within that time period with some reason, justified or unjustified, reasonable or downright embarrassing, for his or her temporary vanishing.

But the officer on duty at the Fairview Mountie detachment that morning was immediately concerned about what Jean told him. The unusual circumstances of this disappearance, the fact that the missing person was of some local prominence, and the well-documented history of acrimony in which he had been unwillingly involved over the years, were sufficient to justify immediate inquiries.

Senior officers were informed and Dr. Abe Cooper's receptionist, Mrs. Brenda Osowetski, the only other person besides Abe to have a key to his clinic at the top of the street, was contacted at her home. She met Corporal Bob Sobol a few minutes later.

She told the police that the previous day at the office, the Wednesday, had been a quiet one largely because Abe was going to a medical conference in Orlando, Florida, Thursday.

Abe had left early in the afternoon to go home to pack for his trip. He was due to fly out of Edmonton International Airport at 6:55am May 6. (The airport is a six-hour drive southeast of Fairview if a driver sticks to the speed limit.) After her boss left, Osowetski had tidied the office and locked up.

Now, some seventeen hours later, she was back unlocking the rear door of the clinic. But this day there was nothing routine about what was an everyday procedure because the police officer was standing nearby. Sobol told Osowetski he intended to remain outside in the street. She was to go in alone because he realized that should there indeed be cause for real concern, any police presence inside the building without a warrant would have immediately jeopardized any investigation and, if it should eventually be forthcoming, any prosecution that followed.

It was somewhere between 9:30 a.m. and 9:45 a.m. and the morning air was still heavy and damp. Within seconds of entering the clinic and flicking on a light in the darkened rear section of the clinic, the receptionist realized that things were decidedly not as she had left them the previous afternoon. The blinds in the reception room were drawn closed, the door to the chelation[2] room was shut, and the blinds in that room were also drawn. Osowetski then saw bloodstains on the rug in the room where Abe conducted the chelation process. She gathered herself and continued to look around. There was a roll of duct tape sitting on a stool that had been moved into the chelation room from its normal area. She had never seen duct tape in the premises before. Abe's chair had been shifted from its usual spot and two typewriters had also been moved.

A newspaper, which had not been there when she had left the previous afternoon, lay on a filing cabinet. An empty garbage bag had been moved from the spot where she'd left it, and on the doctor's desk laid a pen and a pad of paper that, somehow, had mysteriously appeared overnight. Osowetski went outside and told the officer what she'd found.

Sobol checked the exterior of the clinic and satisfied himself there was no sign of forced entry. And then as he was to testify later, even more concerned, he did enter the building in order to check whether there was any injured person or any other persons still inside.

Within minutes, those Fairview residents who were already on the move, including staff and patients coming and going from the nearby hospital, were shocked by the sight of a mini-fleet of blue and white RCMP cruisers assembling at the little white building near the high end of their main street. And their curiosity soon turned to alarm when they saw yellow crime scene police tapes being put up around the building.

The RCMP swung into the process of obtaining a warrant to search the clinic. Highly-experienced criminal investigation officers used to handling major crimes were put on alert in Edmonton, and an urgent bulletin was put out to find Abe Cooper's car. The obvious starting point was Edmonton International Airport some six hundred kilometres away to the south. At 1:41 p.m. that afternoon,

---

[2] In addition to his more traditional practice, Abe was a practitioner of chelation therapy, an alternative medical treatment not without controversy, and one not universally accepted as being beneficial. Its supporters claim the treatment improves metabolic and circulatory functions by use of a process that removes toxic metals such as iron and lead, from the body. The treatment involves the administration of an amino acid, ethylene-diamine-tetra-acetic acid (EDTA) by intravenous infusion.

a car registered to the Abraham Cooper Professional Corporation was found in the airport parking lot.

Even a cursory inspection of the vehicle by the first officers on the scene showed that at this scene too, it would be highly desirable, necessary in fact, to obtain a warrant to conduct a full-scale inspection of the car and its contents. After all, the discoloration on parts of the vehicle, especially around the trunk area, looked like dried blood.

The officers in Fairview and in Edmonton could now only wait to obtain the necessary signed warrants. In the meantime, officers in Fairview confirmed that Abe Cooper was staying in Orlando, Florida. Local law enforcement agencies in the Sunshine State, primarily the Federal Bureau of Investigation, were asked to keep a discreet eye on the convention-attending doctor from the North.

Strangely, given the suspicious nature of the alert they'd received, the officers conducting the surveillance noted that the apparently unsuspecting Cooper seemed totally relaxed and was conducting himself in what they had been told was his usual outgoing manner with other delegates at the gathering.

Back in Alberta, though, things were far from normal.

Dr. Cooper's office, (far left), Fairview Hospital (right).

Chapter Four

News of Doug's seemingly sinister disappearance spread along telephone lines, during chance sidewalk encounters, in gossip in stores, banks, credit unions and gas stations, and in excited chatter in homes and restaurants. Word of the mystery, right here in their little town, swept along just as quickly as a wind-driven brush fire would have done across the wide-open expanse of terrain beyond its limits.

In those early Thursday hours of realization dawning, of recognition that something was seriously amiss with the local doctor, relatives and friends were inclined to clutch at any straw of comfort, no matter how unpalatable it might be. Perhaps, some thought, Doug had met with an accident, maybe he had received a blow on the head and was wandering around in town or in the countryside disoriented and lost. At any second, he might miraculously reappear, safe and sound.

Disturbing as the thought most assuredly was, there might even be some strange relief to be found in the fact that the doctor had suffered a relapse in his alcoholism and had gone on a drinking binge. After all, it did happen to recovering addicts, didn't it? Her phone calls to local motels and hotels certainly indicated that in her isolated desperation of that first night, Jean almost hoped against hope that such a disturbing possibility might ultimately prove to be the case.

Informal searching of the town began that morning. As soon as they became aware of the situation, residents carried out casual checks in their back yards and alleys. Meanwhile, family members[3], alerted by Jean, began the process of setting out for Fairview or at least making arrangements to travel there.

When my nephew, Darren, an Edmonton commercial real estate broker, got the news from his mother, he booked two seats on the next short-hop flight north. He then phoned his brother, Doug Jr., telling him to meet him at the airport. Together, the brothers flew north. Darren's wife, Mavis, and Kimber, Doug Jr.'s wife, followed on a later flight.

Daena, my niece, who had immigrated to Australia and married Gary Williams in 1996, was made aware of the family crisis too. A half world away, Daena, pregnant with their second child, waited

---

[3] See Family Tree, Appendix I, page 176.

with her husband and son for news. Doug was the man who, when his grandchildren began to come into the world, had asked with obvious and constant delight and wonder: "What else is there?" As Daena remembered his words, she too began making travel plans. She knew she had to be with the rest of the family.

At her family's farm south of Edmonton, my sister, Mary Lange, went on full alert for more news. During those first hours, she kept hoping that our brother might walk into the yard just as he had done so many times in the past. The phone, usually busy with calls pertaining to the farm operation, began ringing as soon as people in the area heard the news.

It fell to Mary to break the news to our 88-year-old father, George Schattschneider, and his wife, Mary, in their home in Edmonton. Dad was quick to recognize the seriousness of the matter and said, "It's like what happened in Taber."[4]

I got the news that morning when my husband, Lloyd, called me at work. He relayed the message from Jean that Doug had not returned home from a meeting with Abe the night before and that "there was blood in the office." Stunned, I sorted out a few details and left work to wait at home for further news.

One of my first reactions was to call friends and ask them to pray. I wasn't sure what to pray for. It seemed like a bad dream but I knew from the beginning that we were dealing with something ominous. We needed to pray for light in the darkness that had suddenly come upon us. We could only hope and pray that Doug was safe and that we would soon have information about what had happened.

It was all too overwhelming, but it didn't take me long to decide to go to Fairview. Doug had always 'been there' for me, his kid sister. He and Jean had always welcomed me, who had been the single sister and aunt for so many years, in their home and family. So it was that I set out to join the family circle that gathered together now in the midst of this horror. I traveled two days later with a brief stopover in Edmonton to connect with my father, sister, uncle and cousins.

Our family watched every television news bulletin we could and no matter how many times we saw it, we were equally aghast each time to see the photograph of Doug smiling out at us from the screen. We shared our horror, our disbelief and fear, but were bonded in our love for each other and for Doug and his family. Jean

---

[4] Eight days earlier, a school shooting in Taber, Alberta ended in the death of a high school student and the wounding of another.

was comforted by the fact that our close-knit family support system was so quickly in place. Her younger sister and father were also quick to come and add further aid and succour.

At the Fairview Hospital, the mood was simply shock. Thelma Klaepatch, RN, was to write much later in a victim impact statement:

> I was on the night Jean Snider called to ask if Dr. Snider was at the hospital. Knowing Dr. Snider, we were curious as to where he may be as he always told us where he would be and how to contact him.
>
> He always called us when he returned home so we would know where to contact him if he was needed. He did this for years. I was also present when we heard he had gone to meet with Cooper and immediately I knew it was not good.
>
> We had planned a birthday celebration for him and I had just helped to hang the photo collage on the nursery window with all the staff's signatures and best wishes. It became apparent that something horrible had occurred in Cooper's office and I may never see Dr. Snider again.
>
> The best wishes came down from the window and the birthday cake, as far as I know, never made it into the hospital. It was replaced with a feeling of dread. It was that night that the people of the town asked if the staff would join in a search for him and the nightmare continued to unfold.

Meanwhile the Mounties were continuing their pursuit of clues and conducting other investigations, including their own scans of the township and the nearby country for any sign of Doug. All the time more and more people were carrying out their own individual and casual searches.

As the day progressed and there was still no sign of Doug, it became increasingly obvious to all, including RCMP Staff Sgt. Gerry Tonn, the man in charge of the local detachment, that a full-scale, organized search was going to be necessary – and probably over a vast area. And equally, Tonn knew that the RCMP simply would not, on its own, be able to provide the manpower to conduct such a hunt. On the scale required, it was a job that would have to involve the people of Fairview themselves.

Soon the phones were ringing in the homes of people who, perhaps, had the organizational and people skills to run an operation of such major proportions. One of those people was Gwen Tegart, a local beekeeper, a friend of the family, and a woman whose two grown-up children had been delivered to her and her husband Dave by Doug, just as their son-in-law had been.

Gwen was known locally as the Honey Lady. She had been working in the apiary's wax house and had just gone back to her kitchen to check on the progress of a cake she was baking when she got her first call informing her of the mystery unfolding in town. "It was in the afternoon," she was to recall later. "A friend phoned me and asked 'Have you heard about Doug Snider? He's vanished. He went to Abe Cooper's and he hasn't been seen since.' " Gwen quickly called Jean to offer her support.

David Bloom had been conducting renovation work for Doug and Jean that day, so was one of the first to learn of the growing mystery. Later that day, the Blooms and the Tegarts met at the Snider home where family members were assembling. They discussed the possibility of beginning an organized volunteer search.

In order to get the latest official news on the situation, Gwen and Darren drove the few blocks across town to the RCMP detachment where they spoke with Sergeant Tonn. They left the detachment with a plan of action. They decided a civilian search had to be organized in addition to whatever the police were doing. Darren and several family friends would phone ten people and ask each of those people to call another ten, and so on, to recruit a mini-army of searchers which would be ready to swing into action bright and early the next morning. They went their separate ways and began making their calls.

On the morning of Friday May 7, Gwen Tegart awoke at around 6 a.m. totally aware she faced a big day in her life. She busied herself photocopying maps of Fairview and the surrounding district. She had kept the originals from her days as a Provincial Conservative party worker, including four successful stints as a campaign manager, in the receding years. Although her preparations were sound and efficient, she was nevertheless slightly annoyed at herself for leaving home later than she had intended.

When she swung her truck into downtown Fairview at 8:30 a.m., Tegart was greeted by a sight she would never forget. There must have been nearly one hundred people gathered outside the old, vacant Hemstock store, which the Tegarts bought when it had closed down a year or two before. It was now to become an ideal headquarters for the civilian search.

Friends, neighbours, family members, professional colleagues, patients, and acquaintances of Doug and Jean continued to arrive in the days to come to assist in the volunteer effort. At the very height of the search, a task force of up to 72 three-person teams were out in the field at any given time trying to find even the slightest trace of Doug, with scores more on stand down for rest breaks and re-planning.

Friends and colleagues of Darren also became involved in the search in both the Edmonton and Fairview areas, and friends of Doug Jr. arrived to help after they had written their medical exams.

The main street of Fairview. The building on the left served as the search centre.

Chapter Five

The community response to the pleas to help solve the mystery of what had happened to its doctor was immediate, emotional, committed and magnificent. The scale of the organized effort, once it became apparent, did cause the RCMP some initial disquiet however.

The police requested that the civilian force stay out of the way in town because it could interfere with both the police investigation and search presently going on within in the community limits. An understanding was reached that the town itself, at least in the initial stage, was to be strictly police territory and the outskirts and surrounding countryside the domain of the civilian volunteers to comb ditches alongside local highways and byways, to explore river and creek banks, and to check out barns and all derelict properties.

The huge search effort became a joint affair, a fully coordinated enterprise between the official and civilian forces involved and fuelled by the generosity of food and drink donations from individual citizens and local businesses. When the Mounties had satisfied themselves they had completed their in-town investigation and scene preservations, the volunteers were also quick to hit Fairview's streets, alleys, even its flat business sector rooftops.

Late spring was gently easing into early summer as the first units of volunteers began fanning out across geographic grids pre-determined and distributed to them by Tegart and her lead cohorts. The buds on thousands of trees lining the streets and shading the gardens and yards of Fairview, and in the forests of the majestic Peace Country beyond, had yet to open but it wouldn't be long before the tender leaves they protected would sprout into their full glory.

That could be important, both Gwen and Darren wisely noted. The extraordinarily rich leaf cover soon to come would, after all, hinder any aerial search by making it impossible for any spotter on board a plane or hanging from a helicopter to see anything ... such as a person wandering lost and disoriented on the ground or, heaven forbid, a body.

In the ensuing days, before nature quickly rendered them virtually useless except over open ground, several aircraft would be used in the search. They included that of local farmer Don Weiben who flew countless hours with his son over the endless carpet of fields and open range around Fairview and along the densely-treed banks of the mighty Peace and Smokey rivers which snaked through the tapestry of the land.

At the old Hemstock store on that first full day of searching, the first missing posters of Doug were distributed. One was pasted on one of the shop's large street front windows, and others soon began appearing on lamp poles and on notice boards in other stores, hotels, cafes, restaurants, gas stations and bars in the town.

That first day, the first squads of volunteers went about their vital business clinging to the hope they were looking for a man who was still alive. There were grim and depressing rumors, of course, but the newly raised private army of Fairview was largely in the dark about the gory finds in Cooper's clinic and about his apparently bloodstained car being found at Edmonton Airport.

By now, and inevitably, word of the dramatic events unfolding in Fairview was spreading much further afield too. The local media, including the town's weekly newspaper, the *Fairview Post*, was naturally on the story quickly, but soon the word was being made available to a larger and wider audience in several short paragraphs distributed by the Canadian Press network. Its first wire service story to go across Canada and beyond began:

> The disappearance of a local doctor has triggered a massive search Friday by residents concerned he   may have met with foul play ... Dr. Doug Snider was reported missing Wednesday night after he failed to return from an appointment he'd walked to.[5]

The report included Darren's statement about his Dad:

> I would like nothing better if he walked through the door and said he had bumped his head. But I don't think it looks very good.

There was no mention in that story of anyone else possibly suspected of being involved in the disappearance, but that night on its late-night news program, CBC TV mentioned, almost in passing, that another doctor, a certain Dr. Abraham Cooper, was not currently to be seen in town either.

In the hours to come, the staffs of the local newspaper and radio station would be reinforced by other print, radio and television journalists, first from Grande Prairie, an hour to the south, then Edmonton, six hours away, and ultimately even Calgary, some nine

---

[5] In fact, it had been Thursday morning that Doug was first reported missing.

hundred kilometres south across Alberta. In no time at all, there was a new, ever-mobile, mini-community in town.

The RCMP had tried to keep the Cooper connection quiet, but typical of any small town in any country anywhere, the word was very definitely out. There was still a feeling among most locals that somehow the local doctor would re-enter their lives safely, soundly. Tonn and other investigators already feared the worst, however, considering the grisly reality of what had been found so far at Abe Cooper's Fairview office.

The media wolf pack, sniffing blood but uncertain as yet as to either its source or quantity, was initially at least, kept well at bay by Sergeant Gerry Tonn. From the very beginning, Tonn was determined nothing such as a misplaced or misinterpreted remark to a reporter would interfere with or endanger either the investigation or, if necessary, the course of justice that might later be played out in a courtroom.

But as the media swarm gathered, the veteran Mountie did at least, and at last, concede on the record that the RCMP was treating the Snider affair as "highly, highly suspicious".

On Saturday May 8, with one day's vain searching already in the past and day two getting into full swing, he admitted publicly and officially for the first time that he and his fellow investigators from Fairview, Grande Prairie and Edmonton would be very interested in talking to Dr. Abraham Cooper in connection with Doug Snider's disappearance.

When word got around that police wanted to speak to Abe, his devotees, and there were quite a number of them, quietly began letting their support of him and disbelief he could be involved in anything untoward be known. Shocked as they were, they couldn't come to grips with the notion that the man who had cared for them might have had something to do with Doug's disappearance.

As news reporters descended upon the town, our family developed a plan for responding to their inquires. We were careful not to comment about Abe Cooper. More importantly for us at the time, we hoped that the media coverage would help us find Doug and so welcomed opportunities to speak about him. One such interview took place when my nephew, Doug Jr., spoke with *Calgary Herald* reporter John Gradon.

Gradon later wrote:

The young man's demeanor, his body language, his facial expression, had all spoken starkly of someone weighed down by a special and very personal kind of anguish, Snider wanted to talk about his father, no, needed to talk about him.

In his first chat outside the police station, Doug Snider Jr., shyly and uncertainly at first but more comfortably and more openly as it proceeded, conducted himself with the exceptional dignity and grace which came to typify his family as a whole during the long ordeal to come. The final year medical student at Edmonton's University of Alberta began by talking of the fateful phone call that his father had received on the Wednesday evening basically minutes after his own.

The young Snider did not disclose the name of his Dad's last caller but there was mute understanding as to his identity between the two men talking in the shade of the fir trees outside the Mountie detachment building. Gerry Tonn occasionally glanced out, somewhat anxiously, at them from a window as they talked.

Near to tears at times, the vanished Snider's youngest son said: 'Things don't look good. My father is very well known here, very well liked. He's been here for thirty years and he raised us here. He is an advocate for his family, an advocate for his patients, for the whole community. All he wanted was to provide the best possible medical care for the town.'

The last two sentences, of course, strongly hinted at the dark and intriguing sub-plot the young man knew, and the recently-arrived journalist was getting to know, to be involved in his father's present and desperate plight. Wistfully, the young man said: 'I spoke to him by phone shortly before the other call he got. It was his sixtieth birthday Thursday and we were joking about it. He had just finished a painting and was saying he was going to auction it among the family. I said I'd bid a dollar.'

The gentle smile of loving recall faded and Snider Jr. said: 'My father influenced me and motivated me. I just saw how much he enjoyed what he was doing and how much people in town liked and respected him.'

There was nothing his farm-raised father liked better, he said, than looking at and studying the field crops during his frequent mountain biking outings in the countryside around the town.

After a conversation lasting perhaps half an hour, the medical student and the journalist shook hands and parted, but only for the time being. The doctor-to-be strolled away towards his vehicle in the police station parking lot.

To the journalistic observer he left behind, the young Snider somehow seemed lightened through the opportunity to talk of the father whom he adored and whom he was already and obviously missing, desperately. After all, hadn't someone had to say something about his Dad, for his Dad?

At Doug and Jean's home, the doorbell and telephone rang almost continuously. Visits by neighbors bearing gifts of food and expressions of concern were frequently interrupted by calls from the media and a large network of friends and relatives. Volunteers from Police Victim Services offered moral support to our family, numb and in shock, and relieved some of the pressure for us by answering phones and assisting with other tasks such as airport pickups.

I was delegated to keep family members in Edmonton up to date regarding the situation. They were being bombarded by the news reports and needed to know what was happening behind the scenes. I also fielded many of the media inquiries, always being careful not to divulge information that might jeopardize the investigation and any possible legal proceedings in the future.

It was all so surreal.

Fairview Post, Tuesday, May 11, 1999 — Page B9

Dr. Snider's office
will have locum coverage
effective immediately.

Jean quickly arranged for office coverage.

Chapter Six

On Sunday May 9, the congregation at Heimtal Moravian, our home church near Edmonton, prayed for Doug, our family and answers to the mystery that engulfed us. Members there lit a candle for Doug – a Sunday morning ritual that continues to this day.

Further north, the congregations in Fairview's seven churches included searchers who had temporarily broken off from the hunt. It was Mother's Day and as they gathered to worship, they also prayed for Doug and guidance in their search for him.

At the search headquarters, the searchers were joined by Noel Hill, a highly trained professional search master from Grande Prairie. He announced: "We are now broadening the search. We are as satisfied as we can be that the town has been covered." Hill made little or no change to the comprehensive search plan already being implemented.

Hill said: "It's a huge country out there. We have to base our search from Dr. Snider's last known position . . . his home . . . and start from there. So right now the search covers the rest of the world."

Gerry Tonn was another visitor that afternoon. The RCMP sergeant said of the searchers: "The work they have been doing is wonderful and it's vital they continue to do everything possible. But with no direction to show them to take, there might be some frustration setting in. Our investigation is trying to establish a link that will provide them with a direction to take."

Members of our family, when not participating in the search, checked in regularly at the search center. We were appreciative of the painstaking and caring effort being expended.

The thought of Doug lost and suffering somewhere was devastating. I expect it was that fear that drove many to set out on the search to find him, to bring him home, to let him know that we loved him. It was also a way to keep busy, to do something. We must be able to do something! We were all in a state of shock.

Knowing that this matter was not going to be solved by human efforts alone, I suggested to a couple of the volunteers that we hold a prayer service. Before I knew it, the contacts were made and with the assistance of the community clergy, a service was organized for that Sunday evening at the United Church. It was full to over-flowing.

Leading the congregation in prayer, I pleaded with the Holy Spirit to pray on our behalf, to give us the eyes to see what we needed to see, the ears to hear what we needed to hear and the minds and hearts to know what we needed to know. I prayed that God would grant Doug peace wherever he was.

The next morning, the day when Abe Cooper was due to return to Canada from the Orlando conference, search activities in Fairview began pretty much along the lines of what had become the norm. But during the course of that day an agreement was reached to wind things down for a 48-hour lull period so that everyone involved, the police, search coordinators and the hundreds of townsfolk volunteers could take stock of their progress to date and plan their future strategies.

Abe Cooper's patients, friends, and supporters, probably recovering from the initial shock waves that had flash-flooded their little town, were now, finally, beginning to make themselves heard. Among them were Betty and Jack MacKay. Betty McKay told the media: "It's all very unfortunate for the town. There were lots of people who wanted Dr. Cooper to have his hospital privileges restored. I think he's a very caring doctor ... I just hope both of them turn up and there's nothing wrong."

By that time, there was growing acceptance that something awful had indeed happened to the unfortunate doctor, worse in fact, that he was dead, and would never be seen again. Gwen Tegart and her private civilian army hadn't given up though, and the search was resumed, albeit at a much lower key, in the days to follow.

On Tuesday, May 11, I awoke from a restless sleep with the resolve that I needed to speak to the media. My nephews, Darren and Doug, welcomed the support. Darren had to return home to Edmonton to talk to his young sons who were most concerned about their beloved Grandpa. And Doug Jr. needed to return to somehow, given the circumstances, write his Medical Board exams.

Darren led me towards the media pack hovering below the trees outside the police station that morning, and introduced me, "This is my aunt. Be gentle with her. She has a few things to say."

I started: "I was speaking to Doug only four days before I got the phone call that he was missing. Doug talked about his desire for amiable working relationships within the health care team here.

However, one matter remains unresolved – that is a lawsuit that was filed against Doug and two other physicians in town."

I referred to the prolonged and difficult courtroom proceedings and hearings and the fact that Doug had dearly hoped to have the matter settled before his planned retirement later that year. "It appears my brother's voice has been silenced. He's no longer here to speak for himself … it's important that his voice be heard."

Later that day, I spoke to media again in response to a press release from the RCMP reporting that Doug had likely met with foul play, and that the police were awaiting results of DNA testing from evidence including blood found in "searches of various locations around the province."

Mountie Bob Sobol, the RCMP liaison with our family, was an important contact and resource to us. Sobol gathered evidence in the Snider home. This included, for example, a pop can from which Doug was known to have drunk. It would provide RCMP with a sample of Doug's DNA.

Jean informed Sobol that Doug was wearing a special gold watch he had purchased while in the Yukon and wore only on special occasions. Jean thought he was wearing it when he left for the meeting since it was his birthday the next day. As a matter of procedure, Sobol also gathered information regarding Doug's credit cards. He later confirmed that the cards had not been used since Doug had left his home on May 5.

Within a few days, there was some discussion as to whether there should be a memorial service or celebration of Doug's life. The RCMP could not guarantee that Doug would return alive. The decision regarding the service was postponed until the police's press release.

When it became public knowledge that the police expected foul play in Doug's disappearance, we resigned ourselves to the worst-case scenario, and set May 15 as the date for a memorial service for Doug. I worked with Jean in planning the event.

We wanted to give the community an opportunity to celebrate the life of the man who had been one of its physicians for so many years. Our family hoped that we would have another service later – a burial – in the cemetery of our family's home church south of Edmonton. We continue to hold that hope in our hearts.

On the night before the service, Sobol advised us that Abe Cooper had arrived back in Canada from Florida, and was on his

Family entering church for the memorial service.

Photo: Edmonton Journal

way back to Fairview from Edmonton where detectives had met him as he landed. We were fearful that Abe would have the gall to show up at the service. Arrangements were made to have an RCMP presence at the service with an officer posted outside the church as our family entered.

The Catholic Church, chosen because it was the largest church in Fairview, was filled to its capacity of eight hundred people. Mary and her husband, Art, their family, our father and other relatives traveled to Fairview for the service. A section was also set aside for hospital staff with whom Doug had worked closely for so many years. A line-up of young men in dark suits, Darren's business colleagues, formed an "honor guard" along the back wall of the church.

Elmer Harke, a good friend of Doug's since their teen years, led the service. It was a truly ecumenical event as the local Roman Catholic priest, Lutheran minister and Rev. Beth Macha, the Moravian minister from our home church, all participated in the service.

Although my heart was wrenched, I was honored to offer the tribute to Doug and kept the focus on him. I could not, nor did I want to speak openly about the likelihood that my brother's life had been taken by another person. However, I could at least diplomatically acknowledge the strife that had been so much part of Doug's life in the most recent years. I began:

> Your life has indeed been full, full of love, joy, passion. You have been surrounded by people who love you, and you in turn have given generously of yourself.

At times your resolve to settle differences, to advocate for others and to ensure that the truth be known has made you vulnerable. But we know that it is in your vulnerability and humanity that you have been able to be open to all of us.

As I have talked with people since your disappearance . . . I have consistently heard stories of your patience, gentleness and goodness.

I recalled my brother's love of family, collecting paintings, reading newspapers and love of the outdoors. One anecdote about a hunting trip with Doug Jr., his friends and their fathers brought a few chuckles. When the geese were flying in but not landing, the hunters finally realized that instead of keeping his head down, Doug was looking up to watch the geese. Doug was obviously awed by the wonder of those geese in flight on a beautiful day in the Peace River country.

Doug's problems and weaknesses were not forgotten.

We remember your faith and commitment to living by the Golden Rule. Your experience of God's presence and power in your life was renewed when on April 5, 1994; you became a friend of Alcoholics Anonymous. I remember your eagerness to help others begin that same journey. We, your family, are proud of how you have lived out that commitment during these last five years.

I then drew the congregation's attention to two books positioned alongside the displayed photograph of my brother.

The books by your picture today have been placed there by Ben and Cam. (referring to Doug's older grandsons, Darren and Mavis's boys) The boys remember how you loved to read to them.

In my closing, I tried to sum up the shock, lingering hope and unanswered questions on everyone's hearts and minds.

We can't find the words to express our feelings at this time. Doug, we miss you. We continue to look for you, to pray for answers as to what happened to you. We wonder if there just might be a chance you'll come back . . .

I concluded with a promise from the Psalms,

Turn away from evil and do good
And your descendants will always live in the land.
For the Lord loves what is right
And does not abandon his faithful people.
He protects them forever.

In our hearts, our entire family, the police investigators and most thinking people in Fairview knew Doug was not coming back. The ceremony was a public acknowledgment of the grim realization that he was dead.

Some people were likely curious about our family's decision to proceed with a service at that time. The public was not aware of the evidence that supported the reality that Doug was no longer alive. It wasn't made public until the trial. We are grateful that we honored Doug's life when we did – even in the midst of the mystery.

On that same day, the police canine unit from Edmonton was brought in to assist with the search. Eight days later, the civilian search was called off. The huge effort that had focused primarily on the area in and around Fairview had not provided any clues or answers for the community or for our family.

Jean made a point of addressing the searchers via the media. She said:

> On behalf of my family, I wish to say thank you to all involved in this
> search. The generosity of this community is overwhelming and gives
> us the strength and courage to face whatever the future will involve.

Over the years since then, many have, no doubt, speculated as to what happened to Doug that night and whether his body will ever be found. Some have asked why the police hadn't appealed to anyone in the public who might have seen Abe's Nissan enroute to Edmonton that night. The police had been extremely careful, in fact, not to link Abe to any crime until they had forensic evidence to support a charge.

Those who participated in the search may still be haunted by the experience and find themselves looking in ditches and under bushes even years later. One searcher familiar with the history leading up to this mystery believes that searchers weren't meant to find Doug. Apparently, the person responsible for his disappearance was crafty enough to ensure that the whereabouts of Doug's body may never be known.

Part Two

The Doctor's Roots and Call to Medicine

To evolve
        life does need security
                in the mother
                in the father
                in the home
                        with friends
but above all trust in the spirit
                against all assaults of fear and anguish
                against all the unknowns
                against anything that might destroy
                        the flowering of my life...
life needs
        security and hope
security being
the fundamental basis
                the earth
                        in which life is born.
                                        – Jean Vanier

A career that expresses obedience to our vocation
is the concrete way of making our unique talents
available to the community.
                                        – Henri Nouwen

Chapter Seven

Douglas George Schattschneider was born on May 6, 1939 in Edmonton, Alberta. He was the second child of George and Sophie Schattschneider. Our father was of stout German stock and our mother's forebears were Polish-German. Doug was born between two sisters, Mary, the eldest, and myself, Hazel, the youngest.

We grew up on the family farm south of Edmonton. We were all close, but Mary, four years senior to Doug, was often kept busy with household chores while Doug and I played together in the fields, the woods, and the farmyard. A bond grew between us and largely by coincidence, we followed each other into health care professions with me becoming a nurse and he a doctor.

Mary, however, was still accorded an honoured place as the eldest of our generation. She was our big sister who supported us in the same spirit of generosity that she was to take with her into her adult life and her own family. In the bosom of our home, our parents, people of strong and committed faith, taught through their example the meaning of service to others and integrity in all that they did.

Our father had been hurled abruptly into adulthood at a young age when he left school early to work on the farm after his father suffered a dire arm injury in a horse and buggy accident. Our mother had also been forced to take on adult responsibilities at the tender age of thirteen, when she immigrated to Canada from Poland with her older sister, Katie. Mom started her new life in a new country living with a farming family. After a few years at school, she went to work in Edmonton as a caregiver and housekeeper until she married Dad in 1934.

Mom and Dad lived with Dad's par-

Doug on his way to school.

Sisters Hazel and Mary with Doug.

Schattschneider family Christmas, 1953. Our parents George and Sophie, Hazel, Douglas, Mary, Uncle Ernie. Seated: Grandma Matilda and Grandpa Henry.

ents over a year before setting up on their own on the next quarter of land, the ground that would nurture and provide the roots for their three children. As we grew, our parents instilled us with a deep sense and appreciation of God's love and presence in our lives. We thrived in a rustic environment where farm life offered daily opportunities to experience the wonder of nature and its cycles of life.

Work and play were combined as we turned the simple, necessary chores of life on the farm into fun and educational activities.

Herding the cows along the roads of Strathcona County offered plenty of opportunities to ride our bikes, pick berries, or explore the ditches for frogs and tadpoles. We helped with the seasonal planting work, the harvesting, feeding the animals, gathering the eggs, and milking the cows. We were largely unaware at that stage that the entire process was subconsciously teaching us the importance of cooperation and teamwork.

Each morning we awoke to the friendly roar of a fire crackling in the wood burning stove and to the smell of breakfast being cooked, and then it was off to Otoskwan School, a wooden, two-room facility about two miles distant from our home.

There were frequent visits to our beloved grandparents who lived on the adjoining farm. We relished the chance to play scratchy old records on the family gramophone, or to rummage, fascinated, through the old papers and books with their pictures and stories from yesteryear.

Over the years, we looked forward to family celebrations with three or even four generations present, including nieces, nephews, aunts, uncles and cousins. Our home, though modest, was a hospitable place where folk were often invited for a hearty Sunday dinner after church.

Family life also revolved around the church and community activities. One and a half miles away from the family farm was the Heimtal Moravian Church. The congregation had been established by Moravians who had settled in the area as far back as 1895.

The Moravian Church was the first Protestant church, founded in 1497, as Unitas Fratrum – the Unity of the Brethren – in Czechoslovakia. John Hus was burned at the stake as a heretic for daring to speak out about some of the suspected corruption he perceived to exist in the all-powerful Roman Catholic Church of the day. His followers covertly kept their faith but remained underground until they were given sanctuary on a sympathetic German count's estate in Herrnhut, Germany.

The Moravians, named after the province of Moravia from whence they came, under the leadership of the aristocrat, Count Zinzendorf, later began a worldwide mission movement ministering to people's bodies, minds and souls.

Our grandfather, Henry Schattschneider, had immigrated with his family to the district from Wisconsin in 1900 in order to become part of the new Moravian congregation and to farm in south

Heimtal Moravian church (top left). Otoskwan School (top right). Schattschneider family home (bottom right).

Edmonton. He married our grandmother, Matilda Wesenburg, a Lutheran woman, who had emigrated from Germany when she was a young woman.

The historic commitment to their faith by our Schattschneider forefathers and foremothers became our family's own grounding, and to a huge extent shaped our values and sense of identity. Our parents taught us to stand up for what we believed was moral and right, but we learned over the years that we might pay a price for taking such a stance. However, even when having differences of opinion, it was equally important not to hold grudges or have ill will towards others.

Doug was baptized and confirmed in the church and in his teen years was leader of the district youth group. His faith sustained him in the years to come and was expressed more often by his actions than words. He devoutly remained a member of our home church for the rest of his life. He often returned there for spiritual reconnection with his roots. Many of our ancestors were laid to rest there – our great grandparents, grandparents, and dear mother, who died in 1972.

In 1957, Doug graduated from Salisbury High School, which has the motto, "Sail On." In his valedictorian address to his class, he verbally charted the mantra by which he was to steer his own life and that of his children. He said:

A ship at sea must have a purpose, and a port as its destination....

In navigating his ship, the captain has several instruments to direct him. We, too, possess instruments that we must employ as we tread the waters of the future. The driving force of the ship's propeller must be our ambition, and as we churn the waters, our compass must be our conscience. In making decisions, we must refer to the direction in which the needle points. . . . However, if the ship is to sail the course that the compass indicates, the rudder must be turned. Our rudder must be our will power. We must have the will power to sail in whatever course our conscience indicates.

If we entrust our ship to the guidance of these instruments that God has given us, we will stand against the tempest of the storm and the raging seas.

Doug went on to attend the Faculty of Education at the University of Alberta and after two years there took up a teaching position at Colchester School near Edmonton. He continued to work towards his Bachelor of Education degree, which he completed in 1963.

It was in 1958, as he worked a summer job at the south Edmonton Creamery, that Doug had the chance to meet Jean Pahal, a young woman neighbor whose picture in a local newspaper had captivated him. She was attending the University of Alberta's Medical Laboratory Science Program.

Doug offered her a ride in his car and the courtship began. Two years later, on September 2, 1960, the young couple married.

Our parents George and Sophie Schattschneider, Doug and Jean, and Jean's parents Esther and Art Pahal.

Chapter Eight

Doug and Jean's obvious delight in their love and optimism in their future together looked to have been totally fulfilled when their first-born son, Grant, came into the world a year later.

All was not well however. Soon after the birth, they were told their little boy had Down's syndrome. Their initial shock soon transformed into a determination that, Grant would not be deprived of the love of his family. In a time when institutionalization was very much the norm for any person with a handicap or disability, Doug and Jean decided that for as long as possible, Grant would remain with them and attend community programs designed for children with special needs.[6]

They moved from their Edmonton beginnings to La Glace, a small community in northern Alberta, where Doug accepted the position of principal of the local school. It was there, in 1963, that they were able to rejoice in the birth of their next son, Darren.

Doug was by this time, however, a man standing at a spiritual crossroads. Deep within him, he had for years been nurturing a leaning towards studying medicine. In La Glace, and in light of his first-hand experience of the teaching profession, the medical calling somehow grew in clarity and intensity in his mind and in his heart.

With their two young children in tow, Doug and Jean packed everything up in 1964 and moved back to the city of Edmonton to enable Doug to enter the medical school at the University of Alberta. To make ends meet and support the family as Doug first embarked on, and then continued his lengthy studies, Jean worked in her chosen profession as a medical laboratory technologist.

In 1966, the family grew once more. Their daughter Daena was born. It was also at this time that the Doug and Jean decided on another life change – to officially alter, shorten and simplify their family name from Schattschneider to Snider.

In 1968, the happy, blossoming young family had reason for further major celebration when Doug graduated from medical school. Doug and Jean's devotion to each other and their dedication to hard work had finally been rewarded.

On the completion of his internship and after a few months in a residency program in internal medicine, Doug decided to go

---

[6] In later years, Grant lived in a community residence in Grande Prairie and returned home for weekend visits. It was during one of those weekends in November 1993 that Grant, who had a heart condition, passed away at home surrounded by the love that had maintained him for so long.

The Snider family picture, taken when Doug graduated from medical school, 1968.

directly into general practice. In 1969, he joined the Fairview practice of Dr. Julius and Dr. Hannah Kratz whom he had met during his internship at the Edmonton General Hospital while Hannah Kratz was being treated for cancer.

The doctoring pair was looking for someone to join their practice and Doug came highly recommended to them. In turn, the Kratz's made an impression on Doug, and since he and Jean were already familiar with the Peace River country, they welcomed the opportunity to return. Doug often quoted the Beaver Indian saying, "Drink from the waters of the Peace River and you will return."

For about a year, Doug worked with the Kratz's, until in an amicable parting of the ways, he decided to strike out on his own and set up his own office in town, with Jean managing the practice and providing clinical support in the office. Together, the two began to exemplify a deep, shared commitment to providing excellent medical service to the community. That team spirit was to endure their whole lifetime together.

A local woman, Vi Landry, a qualified R.N., joined them as the practice nurse and became an integral part of the Snider medical concern. Other nurses and office staff worked with the practice over the years.

As a general practitioner in the community of Fairview, Doug became a huge part of the community fabric of the town. This was, after all, the life of which he had ultimately dreamed . . . being a family doctor in a charming small town with all types of inherent ailments to deal with, and the opportunity to meet and befriend all manner of characters and personalities.

He and Jean quickly, joyously, wholeheartedly, adapted to their new lifestyle. They established their deep roots there, seeing the small township as a great place to raise their children, the number of which increased to four with the birth of Douglas Dean in 1972.

Doug enjoyed getting to know his patients and, as a "farm boy" himself, he was at home with the folk of this rural community. Over the span of thirty years, he came to know and care for two or three generations of some families. He delivered children of women he had delivered one and two generations before.

In addition to seeing patients in his office, Doug, sometimes accompanied by his office nurse, often made home visits to those unable to come to see him. He admitted patients requiring acute care to the local hospital, or if and when necessary, referred them to the regional hospital in Grande Prairie or to Edmonton. It was not unknown for him to accompany his patients in the ambulance or transport them in one of his own vehicles.

He usually made his Fairview Hospital rounds in the mornings but when he had particular concerns, he would drop by the hospital other times in the day to check on patients or complete referral letters or medical records.

When people required medical care after hours, they would go to the hospital emergency/outpatient department. It was the habit and custom in Fairview, as in other rural hospitals, for the local physicians to take turns being on call for outpatient visits and for emergencies. Doug knew that he dare not become too relaxed or complacent about responding to emergency situations, and when he was called out day or night, his feet hit the floor without hesitation as he dashed to deal with whatever situation awaited him.

Throughout the years Doug developed a good rapport with the nursing staff, and he openly recognized his dependence on them to care for his patients. Importantly, they knew they could count on him to respond when they called him to see patients requiring medical attention.

He had the occasional, endearing idiosyncrasy that never failed to amuse the nurses and staff. He always wore a tie but on occasion his shirttail flapped over the back of his paints as he breezed through the hospital. And then there were his trifocal lenses, infuriating modern-day contraptions that he never seemed to master and which he perpetually wore low on his nose. Nurses also witnessed his generosity and respect for his patients. Some recall how Doug would often "reach into his pocket to provide money for a meal or bus ticket for a less fortunate individual."

In the early years of his tenure, Doug held medical clinics at Worsley, which was served by a municipal nursing station. He relished these trips into the country and was always supportive of nurses practising in remote outpost settings where they required advanced nurse practitioner skills.

The wonder of birth plus the personal experience of bringing new babies into the world was one of Doug's favorite moments. To the country doctor, new life meant new hope. He loved to see the children he delivered grow up, and as time went on, have children of their own. It was not uncommon, locals knew and appreciated, how Doug on occasion delayed personal plans in order to wait until a patient in labor was delivered. Trips away from the community were often scheduled around the expected delivery dates of patients.

Even when out of town, Doug could be called upon at any moment for his medical skills. On one occasion, when he and Jean were on a fishing vacation at Margaret Lake, he delivered a baby. The mother was on her way to Ft. Vermilion Hospital, but the airstrip there was fogged in. The pilot recalled taking a doctor into the fishing resort just days before so brought her in his plane down on the lake. Doug was only too glad to help.

When he visited patients in the long-term care facilities, while checking on their medical statues, Doug would chat about the good old days, farm and family life or local affairs. In his mind, a successful visit meant evoking a happy memory or a smile. One story that makes the rounds in family and community circles is the one of a delighted older woman patient declaring after a visit from Doug: "You know, that nice young man should be the Prime Minister."

A significant portion of Doug's time was spent caring for people with chronic and terminal illness. Patients and their families testified to their doctor's compassionate care and support during difficult, uncertain times when dealing with their family's health concerns or loss of a loved one. One nurse attributes Doug's faith in God for "his extra dimension of understanding and patience for those who were dying."

In addition, Doug witnessed death from all varieties of accidents and tragedies, a situation that had more and more impact on him as the years rolled by. The longer he lived in Fairview, the greater the likelihood he personally knew the people involved. Dealing with drownings, fire deaths, car crash or farm accident fatalities and suicides gradually took its toll.

In 1976, when a new Fatality Inquiries Act was enacted, he also took on the role of medical examiner. The purpose of the Act was to investigate deaths that occurred unnaturally or unexpectedly. While it was far from pleasant work, Doug saw it as vitally important that he advocate for the deceased, ensuring that everything was in order, ruling out or confirming foul play, and making suggestions for the prevention of future similar deaths.

Doug's practice also involved work as a general practitioner anesthetist, and over the years he took additional courses in anesthesia to keep up to date. This enabled the Fairview Hospital to offer surgical services as long as there was also a physician available to perform surgery. This was an ongoing issue for the hospital. Doug believed it was essential to maintain that service for the community, and tried to ensure that a physician capable of administering anesthetics was available when he was out of the community.

Doug was always keenly aware of the risks related to giving anesthetic and his responsibility for monitoring the patient's status during the surgical procedure. He often gratefully commented on his record of "not having been responsible for losing a life" because of any error of his own. It was said with no boastfulness, but rather

Doug with anesthetic machine in OR.

with a sense of appreciation for the skill and the grace that he had been granted in order to do this work.

When it came to caring for people's mental health and emotional concerns, many thought that Doug was particularly gifted. He believed, in the simplest of terms, that the best mental health care was caring by other people in the patient's life. That included the family physician. One young patient still remembers Doug telling him that if a person were kind to animals, it would follow they would also be kind to their fellow humans.

Doug stops to visit with a patient while making rounds.

Doug often shared stories from his own life and family to encourage his patients. This quality endeared him most to many of his colleagues and patients, giving them the realization that he was very much one of them, and showed he was dealing with joys and concerns similar to theirs. In the words of one of his former colleagues "he didn't let it go to his head that he was a doctor."

Ever conscientious about keeping his clinical knowledge and skills up to date by reading, attending courses and consulting with colleagues, Doug's skills as a rural physician were generally regarded by authorities and peers as being above average. He took his patients' complaints seriously and didn't hesitate to request further testing or a consultation by a specialist. He was constantly concerned about the well being of his patients, frequently reviewing and evaluating his interventions to ensure they achieved the best outcomes for those he was treating.

In 1978, nearly ten years after he'd begun, Doug felt he needed a re-invigorating break from country practice and took up a post in the emergency unit of Edmonton's University of Alberta Hospital. For one year he saw the best and the worst that can be experienced in the emergency department of any major city hospital.

He followed up his Edmonton stay with a year in Fort Vermilion. In 1980, Doug and Jean returned to Fairview with their family. However, a fascination and empathy with the far north combined with a deep appreciation for the northern peoples, led Doug to complete a number of short locums in the Arctic in ensuing years – twice in Inuvik, and twice in Iqualuit, Northwest Territories.[7] The last of these trips was to Davis Inlet and Goose Bay in Labrador in February of 1999, a few months before his death. Although planning to retire from his general practice, Doug intended to return to the North in the fall.

In so many ways, Doug thrived on the challenges of this, his ultimate calling. He was doing what he felt he had been called to do, and he thereby derived great satisfaction from the work. But the pressure was also huge, and some who knew him well even said that he was overly conscientious. His patients' needs often came before his own or the needs of his family who had learned to live with constant interruptions to and intrusions into their lives.

Doug in Labrador.

Doug in his office.

---

[7] Iqaluit is now part of Nunavit which became Canada's newest territory in April 1999.

Chapter Nine

Few people outside our family knew the amount of stress that Doug was experiencing. The long days and sleepless nights were taking their toll, and while Doug's passion for medicine kept him going, it was the politics of medicine that gradually but increasingly made the burden intolerable.

Doug was a man convinced he could always see the bigger picture and believed deeply that there was a dire need for improvements in the system. The practice of medicine has its own politics that can pose considerable strain, especially when discord arises. While physicians are independent practitioners, they do not work in isolation. They are accountable to their professional licensing body, the College of Physicians and Surgeons that sets standards for their practice.

Doctors collaborate with and depend on the work of other health professionals including nurses, laboratory and X-ray technicians, pharmacists, and rehabilitation personnel in the diagnosis and treatment of their patients. Physicians also cooperate with each other to ensure that patients get adequate and appropriate care. As part of the process, they are granted hospital privileges by hospital boards as in Doug's early days of practice, or under the current revised system, by regional health boards.

Hospital privileges are vitally important to physicians, perhaps especially so in rural areas such as Fairview. Hospital privileges give a physician the right to admit and treat patients in the hospital involved, and in return, the physician is required to meet certain expectations such as adequate documentation of treatment and cooperation with hospital staff.

At a local level, the Chief of Medical Staff is appointed by the health board and is the main liaison between the medical staff and the board. Doug served as Chief of Medical Staff at Fairview Hospital many times over the years. That job added even greater pressure and responsibility to what some might have deemed an already excessive workload.

Doug often said he would have preferred not to have the additional responsibility of Chief of Medical Staff, but somehow was unable to avoid it. This was perhaps because of the informal leadership role that had been bestowed upon him. After all, he knew the

Fairview Health Complex.

issues inside out and was recognized as being a strong advocate for the best possible health care for the area.

Under Canada's Medicare system, physicians in Alberta, including those in Fairview, bill and are paid on a fee-for-service basis by Alberta Health Care. Decisions about fees, levels of service and funding for health care facilities are made at a government level. The government also controls the amount and manner in which money is spent on medical education. The Alberta Medical Association represents Alberta physicians' interests and concerns in these matters and is a resource to physicians in maintaining their own professional competency and growth.

Doug strongly believed that country medicine was the poor cousin in the 'medical family'; that it wasn't getting the attention or the resources it deserved and that decisions regarding health care were being made without full knowledge or appreciation of the realities and needs in rural areas. Traditionally, there had always been a shortage of physicians in rural areas. In comparison with large urban areas, there were fewer incentives and resources to attract physicians to and support them in country practice.

To Doug, it seemed that decisions regarding health care spending were largely political and not necessarily made in the best interests of the people either in his own community or the society as a whole. And so he entered politics. Wanting to make a difference, he sought to advocate for his community and hoped to have an impact on the delivery of health care on a broader level. Doug won the nomination to represent the Progressive Conservative party in the Spirit River-Fairview constituency in 1982.

He ran against provincial New Democratic Party leader Grant Notley, an eloquent, highly intelligent and likeable young politician

Electioneering in 1982.

who had for some years represented the constituency in the Alberta Legislature. Doug knew that politically, Notley would be an extremely tough nut to crack. He took a six-month leave from his practice in order to focus his energy on the campaign. He arranged for another physician to take over his practice during that time.

Doug took to the election trail with the same all-consuming passion with which he had taken every other step in his life. One issue that he took on early in his campaign was the question of the building of a small hospital in a riding neighboring his own. He called the proposed construction of a ten million dollar, 25-bed hospital in Grimshaw a mistake, economically, medically and socially. He invited input from local people, consulted with party leaders, visited the proposed site in Grimshaw, and concluded once again that the government's answer to the medical needs of northern Alberta was not based on a logical plan.

He questioned the closing of the Berwyn hospital in favor of a new hospital in another riding without a vote by the people, and

The family in 1981. Standing: Doug, Doug Jr., Darren. Seated: Daena, Jean, Grant.

suggested the alternative of increasing the level of care at Fairview and Peace River Hospitals and a long-range plan for a regional hospital for the North Peace. He maintained that the "H" on highway signs denoting "Hospital" should mean availability of a competent medical team 24 hours a day. The hospital in Grimshaw was eventually built and still continues to function.[8]

Although Grant Notley and Doug held different political beliefs, their respect for each other was evident during the campaign. Doug worked hard to win, put his heart into the campaign, visited constituents, attended forums and listened to people's concerns. There was real optimism in the Snider camp that he would actually win the seat. He nearly did. The final tally on election night, November 2, 1982 placed him only 186 votes behind Notley with the Western Canada Concept candidate coming up stronger than expected.

After the election, Doug's decision was immediate and clear. He would return to his medical practice full time. For many people in the community of Fairview, he made the right choice. They seemed simply pleased to have their doctor back.

Tragically, Grant Notley was to die in a plane crash two years later on his way back to Fairview after a typical working week at the legislature in Edmonton. Doug was quick to note privately that had

---

[8]Ten years after Doug's foray into the political arena, the Alberta government reviewed its decisions to build small rural hospitals and some have been closed down. Instead, the concept of regional health care was implemented in the nineties and Peace River and Grande Prairie became the two regional centers for the Peace River country, something along the lines that Doug had suggested.

he been elected, he could well have been a victim of the crash that had also claimed the lives of other members of the small Fairview community. The crash was a traumatic event for the locals and they long mourned the loss of all the fine people lost.

Back in practice, Doug's commitment to the needs and people of Fairview and his concern about sufficient medical coverage for his community was ongoing. But as in many small communities, there was a regular turnover of physicians – with the notable exceptions of Doug and Dr. Paul Chung.

Doug was open to working with new physicians and often attended recruitment fairs in order to recruit doctors to Fairview. He noted with regret, however, that some new graduates were reluctant to take on the challenges and demands of rural practice. He went as far as appealing to the medical profession to find ways to better prepare physicians for work in rural communities. He believed that if this matter was not addressed, rural communities would receive sub-standard care.

When the news broke that Doug had met with foul play, people reflected on Doug's commitment to his community. One person wrote: "The respect and affection that the vast majority of the community had for Dr. Snider was well earned by his dedication and his work in this community."

A medical colleague in the South Peace area described Doug as an "outspoken advocate for the Region, extending to the Region invaluable and exemplary service, serving the community and his patients with dedicated, selfless service."

A physician, who had worked with Doug and often did locums for him when he was out of town, tells the story of Doug coming to Fairview hospital one night in his pajamas in response to her call for assistance in resuscitating a newborn baby who was not breathing. When asked what kind of doctor he had been, she says simply: "Snider was the kind of doctor who would come in his pajamas if you needed him."

At the hospital, the nursing staff maintained the affable doctor's humour, friendly manner and praise for their efforts had built confidence and inspired them to carry on even when times, as they often were, were tough. One nurse put it this way: "There will never be another like him. Nobody cared about that place the way he did."

Indeed, effective teamwork in patient care requires relationships of mutual trust and respect between the health professionals. When implementing medical orders such as the administration of medications, nurses need clear and specific medical orders. If a nurse carries out an order that is questionable or known to be unsafe, it is the nurse who is accountable. On occasion in Fairview, nurses who had questions about an order or orders developed the habit of calling Doug at home for confirmation or guidance, even though he might not be the physician on call.

Since safe and effective patient care ought always be the physician's primary concern, a physician will most often welcome support of a medical colleague when dealing with difficult medical cases. However, that is not always the case. Physicians are, in fact, private business people and competition for patients (and business) may become contentious.

Particularly in small centres such as Fairview, professional jealousy can and does occur if one physician is perceived to be more successful than another. The major challenge for physicians in environments such as this is to find the best balance in all aspects of their lives.

Clockwise, beginning at upper left: Dawson City cabin, cruising the Labrador coast in 1992, Doug checking the crop, Daena presents her father with a piece of her needlework to add to his art collection (1993), Doug and Jean on their Peace River farm.

Part Three

Facing Controversy

The true measure of a person is not how he behaves in moments of comfort and convenience but how he stands at times of controversy and challenge.

— Martin Luther King Jr.

Chapter Ten

Dr. Abraham Cooper arrived to begin practice in Fairview in 1989. Larger than life, vigorous, ebullient, he made an immediate impression. He struck some folk in Fairview as a true character, likeable but slightly outrageous, the like of which the town had seldom, if ever, seen before.

It certainly wasn't hard to be amused or bemused, or both, by his fanatical love of the martial art, Tae-Kwan do, and the sight of him cruising the streets and highways around Fairview on his powerful Honda motorcycle. He certainly made his mark and in the main, it should be said, it was a favourable one.

Born in Manitoba in 1938, the Regina College graduate had been an administrator with the Canadian Army's Medical Corps in Canada and Europe in the 60s. In 1969 he received a degree of Bachelor of Arts and Science at the University of Saskatchewan and had then entered the University of Manitoba to study medicine.

Cooper graduated in 1973 and completed a series of rotating internships, including a spell in Calgary and time at Calgary's Holy Cross and Colonel Belcher Hospitals. He re-enrolled in the military, this time as a medical officer with the air force. He returned to the University of Manitoba and completed general surgeon studies before practising in the United States, primarily in Montana, Minnesota and North Dakota.

In Fairview, he was initially regarded as a fascinating new face in town, a breath of fresh air, a man's man; in short, a character. Regulars of the morning coffee club that daily held court at what was then The Right Stuff café, halfway up the eastern side of Main Street, comprised a cross-section of the township's more prominent male citizens. The breeze they shot was mostly entertaining and harmless hot air. Numbers varied from day to day, anywhere from three to ten they say, but most mornings, the police officers, the lawyers, the businessmen, the newspaper people, and more often than not, Abe Cooper, could be found hanging out together.

Abe played a major role in the cozy proceedings that were a daily feature on Fairview's social calendar. A fellow club member, businessman Ken Landry says, "He was witty, he was funny. Everyone thought he was kind of eccentric. But he was a good public speaker and an entertainer."

Abe often announced his arrival by smacking one of his already-seated companions on the back of his head. The smack was usually accompanied by a verbal swipe, a hard-edged wisecrack that could hurt almost as much as the physical slap. The coffee-swigging companions put up with it more often than not. His sharp wit could be a tad cruel but, after all, the physician, who was a rock of Rotary and the toast of the Toastmasters, was in the main, fun to be around.

Most seemed to accept him as just someone who enjoyed pushing the envelope. He openly defied and embarrassed his police acquaintances by riding his big motorbike without a helmet during local charity rides and town parades. His unprotected shock of silver hair stood out illegally among his buddies in the district's affectionately labeled 'Geriatric Biker Club'.

Abe liked teasing the police down at the Right Stuff too. He would talk of how to commit the perfect crime – usually how to channel his money out of the country – in front of RCMP Sergeant and club regular Gerry Tonn and other officers. And he often spoke of how certain people and the problems they created might be best dealt with through the efficient use of an axe handle. It was a constant theme, so much so, that the non-police members of the group jokingly presented him with an axe handle bearing the cryptic inscription "Attitude Adjuster".

However, the atmosphere soured whenever Abe returned to the never-ending conflict between he and his medical peers in the town. The friends shifted uneasily in their seats whenever he brought up the matter of the supposed conspiracy against him by the town's other doctors and of the resulting $3.2 million lawsuit that he had brought against Drs. Doug Snider, Paul Chung, and John Clarke.

Ken Landry says: "We didn't like that. After all, we were friends of the other doctors as well. We just wished Abe would drop the whole thing." A friend of Doug's and at one time of Abe, Ken shakes his head. "I can honestly say, looking back, none of us had any sense, any idea, of where all this was going, where it was going to lead." As he talked in the basement family room of his villa home on the west side of town much later, his wife Vi listened from a nearby armchair.

For 27 years, Vi[9] was Doug's faithful friend, nurse and assistant. She and Ken somehow epitomized the little Peace Country town they called home. For while her husband did once call Cooper a

---

[9] Sadly, Vi passed away in August 2004, four years after this interview. In 1994, she had been treated for cancer that returned in December 2000, a few months after the Cooper trial.

friend, Vi Landry said unequivocally: "I couldn't stand him from the minute I met him. Cooper was loud, rude and arrogant. He was a real Jekyll and Hyde."

When it came to Abe Cooper, it seems, there were no half measures.

* * *

Information in this chapter was gathered by *Calgary Herald* reporter John Gradon and featured in the article, "Anatomy of a Deadly Feud", *Calgary Herald*, October 8, 2000.

Chapter Eleven

The history of complaints against Dr. Abe Cooper in Fairview and in turn of the complaints and the counterclaims he made against his medical colleagues in the little town is complex, compelling and chilling.

One of the first conflicts arose when a nurse reported that Cooper had refused to attend the hospital to see a patient with chest pain. In his role as Chief of Medical Staff, Doug was required to investigate the situation.

Cooper's response to complaints about him was often to challenge the credibility of the authorities and other physicians in the community. Cooper threw out accusations that the longer- established doctors were needlessly lengthening patients' hospital stays purely to raise more revenue for themselves. He was hardly endearing himself to his medical colleagues or to a large section of the community by unfavourably comparing circumstances, facilities and methodology in Fairview to his previous experiences in the United States.

The arguments became more frequent, more upsetting, and more spiteful. By the early 1990s, health care in Fairview had basically descended into a state of constant disruption. It was in turmoil, and matters only seemed to be getting worse by the day. So bad did the deterioration become, that health authorities in the community were ultimately forced to confront the conflict that was splitting the town's medical practitioners – and to an extent the town itself – and order an official internal inquiry.

As a result of that, a special code of conduct was drawn up for the Fairview doctors. It was a document they all signed, except for Cooper, who had largely been found to be at fault by the inquiry.

When Cooper refused to put his name to the Fairview Health Complex Code of Professional Conduct for Medical Staff, the Board of the complex did not renew his hospital admitting privileges. Loss of hospital privileges can be a potentially disastrous situation to any doctor in any small town. Such an unwelcome development was certain to bring with it the consequences of a dwindling patient list and a reduced income for the physician in question.

In 1997, Cooper filed his lawsuit against Doug and two other doctors for their part in what he claimed to be a deliberate conspiracy to firstly ruin his reputation and then run him out of Fairview.

* * *

A much more detailed study of legal and health community reports and documents reveals a litany of incidents, a pattern of regular conflict and confrontations and attempts by health authorities to come to grips with what had become an embarrassing and acrimonious fiasco. The documents used for research here span a time period between 1994 and May 5, 1999, the night Abe Cooper phoned Doug and lured him into what turned out to be a dangerous situation, but one from which he could not walk away.

A particularly revealing document source is the final report of the Hospital Privileges Appeal Board of Alberta hearing regarding the Fairview situation May 8, 1998. The report states that prior to Abe Cooper's arrival in Fairview in 1989, the medical staff consisted of Dr. Douglas G. Snider, Dr. S.Y. (Paul) Chung and Dr. John Clarke. It goes on:

> Problems began to emerge shortly after Dr. Cooper's arrival in Fairview.
>
> A series of official patients' complaints against Cooper were received by the hospital's Executive Director and they were all referred to the Chief of Medical Staff, Doug Snider, for investigation and report.
>
> It was determined by him that several of those complaints did not establish a lack of professional competence or conduct on the part of Dr. Cooper.
>
> At the same time the observation was made, to the effect, that Dr. Cooper, when designated as the 'doctor on call', manifested a reluctance to extend himself to attend the hospital to see patients at night.[10]

According to the report, a special meeting of the medical staff was held with Dr. Cooper on December 14, 1992 to review three areas of concern; that is, the completion of outpatient records, non-attendance at the hospital when he was 'doctor on call', and, significantly, his working relationship with nurses. And later,

---

[10] Report of Hospital Privileges Appeal Board in the matter of an appeal respecting the denial of hospital privileges at the Fairview Health Complex; and in the matter of the Hospital Privileges Appeal Board of Alberta between Dr. Abraham Robert Cooper and the Mistahia Regional Health Authority, Province of Alberta, May 8, 1998. All further references to the report in this chapter are from this document.

A special meeting of the medical staff Review Committee was held on May 31, 1993 in order to review four complaints involving Dr.Cooper for the purpose of submitting findings and recommendations to the hospital's board of trustees. Dr. Cooper, although given notice, did not attend.

The 1998 report then states that the medical review committee proceeded with their meeting and submitted its report to the board. On the following day, June 1, 1993, Dr. Cooper forwarded a list of fourteen complaints to the Executive Director of the hospital. The report notes that, with the exception of one serious allegation against Dr. Paul Chung that was not supported by evidence and emphatically denied, "the other complaints are not worthy of comment."

The Hospital Privileges Appeal Board reported:

The Board (of trustees) conducted a hearing on July 21, 1993 and after having heard evidence from nurses, Dr. Cooper and Dr. Snider, the Board concluded that the care provided in respect to three of those complaints was inappropriate and for that reason, Dr. Cooper was given a letter of censure . . .

It is worthy of note to dispel Dr. Cooper's complaint of bias that Dr. Snider, in his capacity as Chief of Staff, investigated complaints made by two patients and concluded that in neither case was Dr. Cooper professionally incompetent.

Several meetings held to deal with the issues festering in Fairview were unsuccessful in resolving the problem. Unable to handle the problem at a local level, officials took it to a higher authority. They asked the College of Physicians and Surgeons of Alberta to investigate the complaints in order to stabilize the medical staff.

Dr. Robert Fraser was recruited to investigate and report on the situation. His final report dated October 13, 1993, came to a number of startling conclusions and he made a number of recommendations. His report concluded:

There is clearly an unhealthy, unprofessional atmosphere in the medical staff which threatens patient care to the extent that services to some may be denied.

And Fraser at least was clear in his own mind as to where most of the blame lay. He reported:

Although conflicts seldom arise from the actions of one person it is clear that Dr. Cooper has been and remains the source of the most clearly identifiable problems. He has accused one or other of his confreres of incompetence, greed, unprofessional conduct, unnecessary medical services, conspiracy to harm him, and psychotic behavior.

Fraser further noted:

Dr. Cooper has shown little concern for responsibilities arising out of his membership on the medical staff of the Fairview Heath Complexes. He has not attended meetings consistently and on at least one occasion demonstrated discourtesy to visiting officials by not appearing to meet with them. He also shows no desire to work with the Director of Patient Care.

As a result of his investigation, Fraser recommended:

1. That an experienced physician be appointed as External Chief of Staff be appointed, preferably from the staff of Grande Prairie's Queen Elizabeth II Hospital.
2. That the Board of the Fairview Health Complex, with the advice of the Administrator, draw up a list of requirements and expectations to be made known to Cooper.
3. That in order to monitor Cooper's success in improving his attitude and actions, he be required to meet monthly for the subsequent six months with a committee consisting of the Chair of the Health Complex Board, the Administrator and the External Chief of Staff.
4. That Cooper's failure to satisfy the Committee that he was making satisfactory progress would result in consideration to suspend his staff privileges.

The Board of the Fairview Hospital Complex implemented Dr. Fraser's recommendations. Soon after the Fraser report was issued, Dr. Robert Staples of the Queen Elizabeth II Hospital in Grande Prairie was appointed Chief of Staff and a Code of Professional Conduct for Medical Staff was prepared and approved by the Board in November 1993.

The code highlighted the expectation that medical staff adhere to Medical Staff Bylaws, and be familiar with and provide services in accordance with the value system of the hospital as expressed in its mission statement.

The code also emphasized the importance of regular clinical appraisal, peer review, and the expectation that "every reasonable attempt be made by the Medical Staff to work together as colleagues." It specified a number of hypothetical matters as examples of breaches that might be cause for suspension, dismissal or non-renewal of privileges.

They were:

Failure to comply with the provisions of the Medical Staff Bylaws, Rules and Regulations, and Policies of the Health Complex, or any direction or Order issued by anyone having authority to do so under the Bylaws, Rules and Regulations or Policies;

Failure to maintain an acceptable quality of medical care;

Failure, without justification acceptable to the Board, to attend three consecutive regular meetings of the Medical Staff or a committee of which he/she is a member;

Failure to complete a patient's record as required by legislation or by the Board;

Exceeding the limits of his/her privileges, except in the case of a medical emergency;

Failure to cooperate with other members of the Medical or Health Complex staff;

Impairment due to drugs, alcohol, physical or mental health;

Unprofessional conduct;

Disruptive behavior;

And such other grounds which the Board believed necessary for the proper administration and operation of the Health Complex.

The Fairview code also included the Code of Ethics of the Canadian Medical Association prepared by physicians as a guide and standard for physicians' ethical behavior.

The unique Fairview Code of Conduct, as mentioned before, was immediately and willingly signed by all members of the local medical staff – all except Dr. Abe Cooper that is.

The Hospital Privileges Appeal Board report said:

When medical privileges were reviewed for renewal by the Hospital Board of Trustees in early 1994, Dr. Cooper's privileges were extended until only March 23, 1994 because of his objection to accepting a Code of Conduct endorsed by the other three doctors.

At a meeting of the Hospital Board on March 23, Dr. Robert Staples spelled it out as he saw it. He stated:

Dr. Cooper has limited interest in looking ahead in terms of working as a progressive member of the medical staff, but appears to be concentrating his energy on digging up dirty laundry on other medical staff members as he feels has been done to him.

The Board of Trustees' decision was clear. They resolved that "Dr. Cooper not be re-appointed to the active medical staff effective April 1, 1994." However, he was granted laboratory, X-ray and physiotherapy privileges and was allowed to attend to his three long-term care patients.

The Hospital Board also decided to request an urgent and complete external audit of the medical staff by the College of Physicians and Surgeons. As a result, the College appointed Dr. Guy Goikert, Dr. John Gammon and Joanne Ward, a nurse administrator, to conduct the audit on May 8, 9 and 10, 1994.

After their inquiries, Goikert noted "that the medical staff worked well together without the conflicts created by Dr. Cooper."

Ward stated that she perceived that "nursing staff felt uneasy, intimidated and degraded by Dr. Cooper. He was described as arrogant and uncooperative."

The recommendations were far-reaching but one was particularly precise. The College audit panel recommended:

That Dr. Cooper's remaining privileges be immediately terminated, thus limiting his access to the hospital and easing the tension caused by his presence.

Abe Cooper was not one for giving in easily and was already planning his next move. His appeal to the Hospital Privileges Appeal Board heard on June 29, 1995 determined that:

due to noncompliance by the Board of Trustees with the medical staff bylaws, Dr. Cooper's privileges should be reinstated.

The Court of Appeal upheld the decision.

On April 1, 1995, due to provincial government restructuring of health care in Alberta, the Mistahia Health Region Board (renamed Peace Country Health Region in 2003) assumed administrative responsibilities for the Fairview Health Complex. The new Board soon became acquainted with the Fairview tinderbox. It held a hearing on August 15 and 16, 1995 to:

reconsider renewal of Dr. Cooper's privileges and it arrived at a decision to deny renewal beyond September 10, 1995.

A letter dated September 8, 1995 was sent to Dr. Cooper to inform him that renewal of his privileges had been denied. That letter listed four reasons for the denial which were later summarized in the Appeal Board report as stemming from:

> the fact that in its judgment he was a disruptive influence at the complex due to his inability to work in harmony with the other members of the medical staff.

The hearing of the Hospital Privileges Appeal Board in 1998 was to review that decision. The Board reviewed approximately 315 pages of evidence submitted by Cooper. Their report noted that his evidence revealed:

> the factors which led to the disruptive problems with the Health Complex created by his presence. He expressed his distrust of the motives and competence of the members of the medical staff and of the nursing staff – and as well his apparent lack of respect for the Hospital Board. His general attitude and the opinions he expressed regarding his medical colleagues and the administration created an atmosphere of conflict, friction and frustration hardly conducive to a harmonious collegial relationship within the Health Complex.

The report made the following observation and drew the conclusion:

> It is most significant, in the opinion of this Appeal Board, that before Dr. Cooper was granted hospital privileges, Drs. Snider, Chung and Clarke co-operated on a professional level; worked together to function as a medical staff unit notwithstanding their personal differences and notwithstanding the personal problems experienced by Dr. Snider and Chung; and also despite the fact that they were not socially compatible. It is well documented that after Dr. Cooper's admission to the medical staff the functioning of the medical staff suffered for lack of harmony and trust . . .

> It is this Appeal Board's finding and conclusion that Dr. Cooper was a disruptive influence in the Health Complex and that he is unable to work in harmony with the medical staff and indeed with the nursing staff and the administrative staff as well.

> In our view the reasons conveyed to Dr. Cooper by letter dated September 8, 1995 for denying a renewal of his privileges is fully justified. There is ample evidence to support those reasons.

The report refers to a decision from a previous appeal that:

lack of cooperation of a medical staff member of a hospital is a legit-imate ground for denial of hospital privileges. Dr. Cooper's disrup-tive tactics and his failure to get along with the other members of the medical staff stems from his inability to cooperate.

It was then stated, for emphasis, that:

All members of this Appeal Board concur with this decision.

Chapter Twelve

Abe Cooper then made another appeal to the Alberta Court of Queen's Bench. His submissions appeared to observers to be focused on the issue of who "was to blame" rather than "how is the problem best resolved". The decision in that final appeal, dated March 9, 1999, was to uphold the decision of the Hospital Appeal Board for the same reasons already given in previous decisions.[11]

In addition to repeatedly appealing the decision regarding his hospital privileges, Cooper took legal action against the hospital board and his medical colleagues.

On October 27, 1995, he filed a civil suit against the Mistahia Regional Health Authority, Dennis Magnusson, past administrator of the Fairview Health Complex and Doreen Makarenko, who was chair of the Fairview Hospital Board of Trustees when the initial decision was made to deny Dr. Cooper hospital privileges.

And on July 8, 1997, he filed a suit against his three medical colleagues, Dr. Soong-Yi Chung, Dr. Douglas G. Snider and Dr. John Clarke. The suit was activated in March 1999 when Cooper learned he had lost his latest appeal. He claimed that they had:

> wrongfully and maliciously conspired and combined amongst themselves to injure him in his business as a physician and a surgeon.

He named a number of acts which he claimed were carried out by the defendants "in pursuance and in furtherance of the said conspiracy". These included:

> encouraging and inveigling hospital staff and patients to create incident reports and complaints respecting the Plaintiff (Cooper) with a view to affecting negatively his ability to carry on his business as a physician and a surgeon.

Further, he claimed:

> the said conspiracy was conducted for the purpose of causing damage to the Plaintiff by making it difficult for him to represent and act for his patients thereby resulting in financial benefit to the defendants and each of them.

He claimed damages totaling $3,200,000. Proceedings for review of this claim actually repeated many of the claims that had

---

[11] Report of judgment of Honorable Justice M.B. Bielby, Alberta Court of Queen's Bench; Cooper vs. The Hospital Privileges Appeal Board, March 9, 1999.

been made against his peers in appeal hearings. The defendants were not present to hear the testimony against them.

Pre-trial examinations for discovery (a legal procedure by which one party gains information from the adverse party that is necessary for the other party's case) began in April, 1999. Dr. Clarke was examined for discovery on April 16 and Dr. Chung on April 20, 1999.

Doug was also scheduled to testify at that time. However, time ran out and he was rescheduled for discovery in July.

Chapter Thirteen

Review of the preceding events appear to show that Cooper's focus was on his hospital privileges, a necessary source of income, and his repeated attempts to first, clear himself of all disruption involved, and instead to place the blame squarely on others.

But what effect did these claims have on those who acted in good faith in what they viewed to be in the best interests of patient care? The primary goal of the health care team at the Fairview Health Complex was, after all, the provision of safe, competent and ethical health care for the community.

Instead, vast amounts of time and effort were spent dealing with the conflict issue, and in that there was a considerable emotional and financial cost.

The people who made the initial complaints and actions regarding Dr. Cooper's conduct could be considered whistle blowers. Whistleblowers are:

> people who expose negligence, abuses, or dangers such as professional misconduct or incompetence, which exist in the organization in which they work. [12]

Such action requires that the concern be properly reported to those in authority for investigation. If the problem persists and action is not taken, it becomes an ethical issue. Not acting or remaining silent may place patients at risk. But when health professionals exercise moral courage to do what they believe is the right thing to do, there may be negative consequences.

Paradoxically, one of Cooper's defence mechanisms was to claim that he was the whistleblower in the Fairview situation. But making allegations in order to undermine a colleague's practice and reputation is a far cry from reporting unprofessional conduct in order to ensure safe, ethical, professional medical practice.

The initial complaints regarding Cooper were reported to superiors and dealt with according to the reporting protocol within the hospital system. They were taken seriously, properly investigated and reported to the appropriate next level of authority for action.

However, it is not uncommon for intimidating actions and threats to be directed towards those who draw attention to a problem. One discussion of whistle blowing and professional responsi-

---

[12] Canadian Nurses Association Ethics in Practice, November, 1999.

bilities notes the danger of accusation as a consequence of such action.

> Alleged wrongdoers might take action in an attempt to cover up inadequacies, to discredit or to retaliate against the whistleblower.[13]

Examples of such accusations can be identified in the accounts of Cooper's retaliatory activities. Investigators consistently identified those actions that held the health care system and the community hostage to the series of threats, accusations and appeals.

Staff in the health care complex did not speak publicly regarding the events surrounding Cooper's privileges. Rather, his retaliatory legal actions ensured that any such opinion and evidence was silenced. The staff would always have been unlikely to discuss concerns publicly at any time during the proceedings. But Cooper's lawsuit certainly ensured their continued silence. And that fact, in many ways, made it impossible for the continuing concerns to be addressed.

On April 5, 1994, shortly after Cooper's initial loss of privileges, the local paper, the *Fairview Post*, reported on his plan to appeal the decision. The doctor was quoted as saying that the removal of his privileges was "an attempt to denigrate him and his work" and likened the Board's actions to a kangaroo court.

In the same report, the Board Chair, Doreen Makarenko, emphasized that in order to provide quality service, the board needed a co-operative and trusting medical staff and in an attempt to ensure a satisfactory situation was reached, an audit of all medical staff had been requested.

The community was understandably concerned and confused over the debacle. For years to come, their questions were being raised in public meetings, in the local newspaper, and in local coffee shops and living rooms. This, after all, was their health care system; the system they expected would look after them.

Throughout it all, Cooper continued to practice in his office less than a block from the hospital. He continued to meet regularly with leaders in the community and had, it seems, successfully convinced at least some he was the victim of unfair treatment. People deserved to know the whole story but would anyone dare speak out and risk the consequences?

Although Doug was no longer Chief of Medical Staff, he continued to feel a moral and professional responsibility to the hospi-

---

[13] Bok, S., Ethical Issues in Professional Life, 1988, 332.

tal and the town for settling the ongoing controversy. He hoped that everyone could get on with their lives and that the community would get the medical care it deserved. He frequently talked with family and friends about his desire to resolve the matter.

And he took his quest further. In a letter to the *Fairview Post* on June 10, 1997, he made a very public appeal for assistance in addressing the problem. He wrote:

> I was chief of the Fairview medical staff when I responded to the public's written complaints to the board about Dr. Cooper's failure to see emergency patients when he was on call. The specific complaint resulting in his loss of privileges was failure to see a patient with cardiac chest pain.
>
> Fortunately in 1989-94 we had an effective decisive board that proceeded slowly through the legal process to protect the public. Unfortunately, a 1997 lawsuit and threats of lawsuits are determining the quality of health care provided in your hospital. Chelation services by Dr. Cooper are not the issue.
>
> We need our present physicians and nurses to provide continued health services. Recruiting physicians is impossible without the closure of the Dr. Cooper hospital privilege issue. Dr. Cooper delayed his own appeal process on May 26, 1997. Our professional goal is to provide continuous, safe, scientific-based, compassionate medical services in your community.
>
> We need the honest reporting by the *Post*, the support of the leaders of this community and the help of our College and Physicians of Alberta if we are to continue to serve you.
>
> Democracy works when the people have freedom of information. Help us to make democracy work in your community.[14]

Doug did not take lightly his action of going public but saw no other way of resolving the problem.

The accusations continued.

---

[14] Letter to the Editor, *Fairview Post*, June 10, 1997.

Part Four

Taking Inventory and Seeking Serenity

Having had a spiritual awakening as a result of these steps,
we tried to carry this message to alcoholics,
and to practice these principles in all our affairs.
— Step Twelve, Alcoholics Anonymous

Chapter Fourteen

The strain on the participants caught in the midst of the decade of turmoil in Fairview took its toll. Dr. John Clarke saw that the situation was not going to change and left town. Dr. Paul Chung developed nasopharyngeal cancer.

In Doug's case, his alcohol abuse escalated to a point where cracks in his drinking regimen and discipline began to appear. Doug, a non-drinker in his youth, had begun using alcohol for the relief of stress earlier in the course of his medical career. The additional stress of Fairview's health care problems likely exacerbated the problem.

The insidious nature of alcoholism, the disease, is such that it is often impossible to pinpoint the cause of someone giving themselves up to its dark, often deadly, clutches. It is often caused by constant over-indulgence becoming a physical and psychological dependency or it can be genetic in nature.

The progress of Doug's alcoholism seemed to parallel the long and distressing litany of traumatic medical meetings and legal hearings related to Abe's conduct and grievances. Many of the critical meetings with Abe were taking place as Doug was also grieving the loss of his eldest son, Grant, who died in November 1993.

Publicly, Doug's drinking problem first came to light when, unwisely but no doubt with the best of intentions, he appeared at Fairview Hospital one evening to tend a patient. It wasn't hard for any close by to smell alcohol on his breath.

Doug was not officially the physician on call that night, but when nurses appealed for his assistance with a patient whose condition was giving them genuine concern, he responded immediately. Dr. Dietrich Wittell reported the matter to the Alberta College of Physicians and Surgeons, and soon Cooper was preparing his next strategy.

The Physician Assist Program of the Alberta Medical Association had been made aware of Doug's drinking in 1993 when his colleague, John Clarke, had observed that Doug had been drinking and therefore unable to take call one Sunday. The goal of the Physician Assist Program was not to discipline doctors with substance abuse problems, but to encourage and assist them in getting help. Clarke had inquired how best he could support Doug in his growing difficulties.

Doug was well aware that he was being monitored. And on April 5, 1994, when it finally became apparent to him that his drinking was affecting his practice, he quit. He agreed to accept help and two months later voluntarily entered a renowned centre in Atlanta, Georgia, for treatment for his alcoholism.

Despite his agreement to do so, Doug entered the painful treatment process, like most who do embark down that difficult road, with some degree of denial remaining in his psyche. However, he was to maintain later that as his mind cleared without drink, his resolve to finally quit, once made, was a conversion experience just as clear and as well defined as that he had felt on entering the medical profession.

Although the treatment in Atlanta was normally scheduled for a period of three months, Doug, like so many before him at that and so many other treatment centres, remained there for a longer period. In all, he stayed a total of six months that allowed for an additional period of treatment reinforcement and for more time to remove any lingering vestiges of denial of his addiction.

There were two driving forces in his ultimate acceptance of his alcoholism and the final commitment to do something about it. First, he desired to continue practising medicine safely. Secondly, he quite simply abhorred and dreaded the thought that one day, in a future near or distant, his beloved grandchildren would see him drunk.

His drinking had begun mainly in private and usually on his day or weekend off call. Sadly, and common to many drinkers at risk, he had found that alcohol seemed to aid in easing the stresses tearing at his life. As with all alcoholics – and people can become afflicted very quickly even after a lifetime of abstinence – drinking became a regular affair, a norm in life, and in the year before he finally quit, it had escalated in dramatic fashion.

Added to that was his consumption of diazepam (valium). He had earlier been self-conscious of a tension tremor that was troublesome when he was administering treatments and had been prescribed diazepam and propanolol for the affliction. The habitual mix of drugs and alcohol became overwhelming.

Our parents had always been non-drinkers and we grew up accustomed to that way of life too. Just prior to entering treatment however, Doug, through personal research, had become more aware of a family history of alcohol abuse playing a part in the lives of our Polish relatives.

Doug's drinking was torture to our family. Not that he was ever violent but his denial, an integral part of the disease, made life extremely difficult for everyone. He refused to believe the warning signs or listen to our appeals for him to see that his drinking was a problem. We could only watch helplessly as his addiction took its inevitable and remorseless toll on the man we loved.

But somehow, in that way alcoholics always contrive in the beginning, Doug managed to hide his personal nightmare and that of our family from the outside world. Somehow, until that night in the Fairview Hospital when he turned out to tend to a patient, he had largely managed to keep his secret away from public scrutiny.

However, when Doug returned to Fairview in December 1994 following his treatment in Atlanta, he was refreshed, ready and capable of returning to his practice. He had agreed to make adjustments in his schedule and to cut back on his obligations in order to reduce the demands and stress in his work and, specifically, he would no longer administer anesthesia or take on the responsibilities as Chief of Staff.

In this way, Doug was freed up to do the work he enjoyed most: caring directly for patients. Now open about his own alcoholism, he used his experience to help some of his patients also come to terms with their addictions.

Those patients, to this day, tell stories of his encouragement and support to them even when he met them on the street. Knowing that he understood and wasn't judging, helped them be honest with themselves and to find the courage to face their own problems. Doug attended Alcoholics Anonymous meetings regularly and often invited folk to attend with him.

In keeping with his agreement when he returned to practice, Doug was monitored by officials of the Continuing Care Committee of the College of Physicians and Surgeons, reporting in for regular drug testing. The results were consistently negative.

Doug returned to his favorite pastimes for enjoyment and relaxation. He and Jean enjoyed trips into the country and to their Peace River farm on their days off. When in Edmonton, they often took in an Edmonton Oilers game, a movie or even a theatre production.

In addition to his professional reading, Doug faithfully read the daily newspaper and sometimes turned to a popular history book written by Pierre Berton, or a John Grisham legal suspense novel. He took up painting, a hobby he had enjoyed in his youth. Ironically, he was to complete a painting of one of his and Jean's favorite places of retreat, a family cabin in Dawson City, Yukon, on the very day he met with foul play.

Above all, Doug's favourite outings during his last five years were those he and Jean made to see the grandchildren. Their two older grandsons, Ben and Cam, sons of Darren and Mavis in Edmonton, were growing up quickly. They were old enough to look forward to special times with their Grandpa who loved to read them stories and tell them about places he'd been. The grandchildren still have a collection of books with notes inscribed by their Grandpa.

The family in Australia was further away so visits were less frequent but regular contact with Daena and Gary was maintained by phone. Doug and Jean did visit Australia in the fall of 1997 soon after Cooper Douglas[15] was born, and they were eagerly anticipating another trip in the fall of 1999 to greet another grandchild expected in September.[16]

Doug thrived in his role as Grandpa and often said it was the grandparent's duty and privilege to teach the grandkids about their family history and its traditions. He had so many fond memories from his childhood that he wanted to share with the kids.

In reality, he was now spending the time with his grandkids that he hadn't been able to spend with his own children. Doug's colleagues and friends described him as "the proudest Grandpa they'd ever seen."

Throughout it all a cloud still hung over him. His concern for health care in Fairview still weighed heavily on him, though now in sobriety. Doug might have changed his ways, but Abe Cooper was apparently making no effort at all to change either his attitude or behavior and continued to be a huge worry. Doug appealed for help but couldn't understand why Abe wasn't being monitored and held accountable by the regulatory authorities in the same way that he was. Apparently, protocols for monitoring substance abuse didn't apply to disruptive behavior by physicians.

---

[15] Because of an unfortunate coincidence, the family later changed the child's name to Douglas Carl.

[16] Jean Snider made that trip on her own in October 1999 to meet their first grand daughter, Brianna Rose. Another granddaughter, Jacqueline Lee, was born to the youngest Snider family, Doug and Kimber, in July 2002. The family often reflects on how proud their Dad would now be of his young family.

After losing his latest appeal regarding his hospital privileges in 1999, Abe activated the lawsuit against Doug and other two colleagues. Confident that since there were no real grounds for the lawsuit, Doug hoped it could soon be settled. Unfortunately, there was no forum for mediation and establishing the truth. It seemed that Abe Cooper, to his targets at least, continuously took advantage of the vulnerability of others, including Doug, and managed to maintain control of the situation by projecting the blame onto them.

More and more, Doug resented being silenced, and in effect, being terrorized by Abe's tactics, but he did not wish him harm nor did he want to force him out of the community. In fact, he repeatedly stated he hoped that Abe would take responsibility for his actions and if necessary get the help needed to come to terms with the situation.

So as time for his retirement drew ever nearer, Doug continued to be as concerned about the community as he was for himself. He desperately wanted to know that the situation was stable when he left.

There are indications of his torment and concern in 31 pages of notes he personally took during the examinations for discovery regarding the lawsuit. During the hearing mere weeks before his death, Doug listened and on lined paper noted his comments on the proceedings, and even went as far as writing his thoughts on how best to answer questions when his turn to testify came.

At one point Doug noted:

> I will say that I privately, strongly counseled Cooper to talk to a friend, colleague about how he (Cooper) felt.

He also wrote:

> My reply would be...we wanted to do everything legally right.

There's mention of a point when, apparently, Paul Chung and Doug had a discussion about whether "fighting to the death" to ensure Cooper did not return to work was appropriate. Doug wrote:

> My reply was that I did not consider this possible because it would not be safe. Nurses could not work with him and follow his orders.
> I love community more than Cooper.

In another reference to the people of Fairview, Doug comments:

> Dr. Chung continues on the stand. I admit resentment as I drive to the Provincial Building passing Dr. Cooper's office – he is working today – with cars lined up including a usual B.C. license to receive chelation. Meanwhile our patients are the losers.

Despite his stresses, Doug did not relapse to drinking. He remained firm in his commitment to his own recovery and was sustained by his renewed spiritual faith expressed well in the Serenity Prayer of Alcoholics Anonymous.

> God grant me the serenity to accept the things I cannot change,
> The courage to change the things I can,
> And the wisdom to know the difference.

He made progress towards the goal of serenity as he stopped to enjoy the simple things in life and he also tried very hard to think of his work as 'just a job' and by doing so be less burdened by the big issues. However, that was not consistent with the person he was and his dedication to medicine.

Nor could he let go of the hope for resolution of the problem that was affecting not only his own peace of mind but also that of many within the Fairview health care community. It was a problem that was standing in the way of recruitment of new physicians for Fairview. He was now able to move on since another physician, John Andreiuk, had agreed to take over his practice. Doug was relieved to know that a skilled physician with knowledge of the region was coming to take his place. Now, if only the suit could be settled and settled quickly.

Doug had looked forward to the discovery hearings related to the lawsuit in April 1999 as another step toward that resolution. However, there was yet another delay. When Doug did not get his turn to testify at the discovery hearings and another date was set for July, he was disappointed but determined not to let this stop him from enjoying life. After all, enough time and energy had already been spent on this unfortunate affair.

Over the years of various deliberations with Abe Cooper, Doug at times publicly expressed the wish that these matters could be settled without lawyers. He stated often he longed for an opportunity to sit down and have a man-to-man talk with Abe and appealed for help in that regard.

After all, wasn't it reasonable to expect that two physicians who were guided by the same principles and code of conduct should be able to work this out? Many who knew Doug saw him as the "eternal optimist" who expected and looked for the best in people and situations. But he was also aware that his dealings with Abe Cooper were not to be taken lightly and were even potentially dangerous.

And so it was, that when Abe called Doug inviting him to a meeting, the latter responded apparently without hesitation. This was the opportunity he was waiting for. Although he had to know that this was dangerous business, he simply could not stay away.

And it cost him his life.

Part Five

Waiting for Justice to Unfold

Although the legal and ethical definitions of right are the antithesis of each other, most writers use them as synonyms. They confuse power with goodness, and mistake law for justice.

— *Charles T. Spalding*

Conscience is the root of all true courage. If a man be brave let him obey his conscience.
— *James Freeman Clarke*

Chapter Fifteen

On May 17, 1999, twelve days after Doug had disappeared, Abe Cooper re-opened for business at his clinic near the hospital.

He had talked to police and had defiantly told them and anyone else who asked he knew nothing of Snider's disappearance. On the surface, for him at least, it was a case of life being back to normal, even in a town divided by a mystery of such depth and suspicions of such intensity.

To the casual visitor or patient dropping by his office, the only tell-tale sign was literally a sign on the door. *Edmonton Journal* reporter Lisa Gregoire wrote later:

Dr. Abe Cooper ordering media off his property on the day he reopened his clinic in Fairview.

Photo: Edmonton Journal.

> A sign soon appeared on the office front door advising reporters to stay away. He had earlier warned reporters to stay off his property.[17]

But the drama took another huge step forward May 27, 1999 when police visited Cooper in Grande Prairie and arrested him. Four days later, in Peace River, he appeared in court to face a charge of the first-degree murder of Doug Snider.

Gregoire's report noted:

> Dr. Abraham Cooper, 60, dressed in a burgundy sweater and brown pants, stood stoic and motionless in the prisoner's box after spending the weekend in Peace River RCMP lockup charged with killing Dr. Doug Snider on May 5.
>
> Courtroom No. 2 was packed with the usual Monday morning list of area offenders. Cooper stood with his hands clasped before him as provincial court judge J. Richard McIntosh read the charges.[18]

Regardless of where they all stood on the Snider-Cooper issue, it was perhaps on this day that the full gravity of the events that had befallen them and their town truly struck home for the residents of Fairview.

---

[17] "Cooper back at work at Fairview clinic," *Edmonton Journal*, May 18, 1999, A6.

[18] "Doctor hears charges in packed courtroom", *Edmonton Journal*, June 1, 1999, A5.

An all-day bail hearing was held June 4 in Peace River, but Cooper was refused his freedom. A few days later, the dates for a preliminary hearing into the matter – August 16 to 20, and August 30 to September 3, 1999 – were set. Cooper was to remain in custody in the time leading up to the preliminary inquiry.

The courtroom was packed with members of press and public for the preliminary inquiry but as the law requires unless there is a special decree by the judge, no reporting of the case details emerged. The inquiry began and ended in Peace River in order to accommodate local witnesses. However, the bulk of the sessions in between were conducted in the courthouse in Edmonton.

Mary and I, our cousin Dave, and Doug's daughter-in-law Mavis traveled back and forth between Edmonton and Peace River in order to attend all sessions of the inquiry. Mary's oldest son Bill travelled from Australia to attend the first part of the inquiry. Other family members attended when they could, but since Jean, Darren and Doug Jr. were witnesses, they were not allowed to be in the courtroom unless they were testifying.

On September 20, Justice John Maher spent two hours summarizing the case and ended by ordering Abe Cooper to stand trial.

After postponements due to Cooper suffering back spasms, he was arraigned in court in Edmonton on December 8, 1999, and officially pleaded "not guilty" to the charge of first-degree murder.

Trial was set later for September 2000 in Edmonton.

Pilgrimage to Peace River farm by Mary, Dave, Jean, Hazel and Bill while attending the Preliminary Inquiry in Peace River, August 1999.

Chapter Sixteen

On Tuesday September 5, 2000, the courtroom on the upper floor of the Court Building in Edmonton was packed. Four hundred prospective jurors had been called to be present for consideration as jurors in the upcoming trial. Much of the first day was spent reviewing reasons why those summoned could not serve on the jury for the trial that was expected to last for six weeks.

There was, understandably, deep concern among the legal authorities about the massive amount of pre-trial publicity surrounding the case even though the trial was to be held in Edmonton, a six-hour drive away from the scene of the alleged crimes in Fairview.

As always in such cases, names were called and the prospective jurors were interviewed briefly by counsel for both the prosecution and defence to establish any pre-determination of guilt or innocence, any perspective, any opinion, that might unfairly influence the decision they would eventually have to make. Some didn't even get as far as the well of the court before something – appearance, gait, youth or age – brought a 'Not Required' from one of the counsels.

During the continuing selection process, a rarely-used method of completing the jury was put into place. As the early jurors were selected, they themselves became part of the process of picking the remaining jurors. Acting as juror-judges, they took part in later interview processes and helped the court determine the suitability or otherwise, the impartiality or otherwise, the acceptability or otherwise, of the later interviewees.

The process is called "cause for challenge", and according to prosecutor David Stilwell, was introduced in this case "strictly as a consequence of pre-trial publicity". It seemed to work.

Almost at the end of the second day, with a jury of eight women and four men having finally been selected, Abe Cooper rose to his feet, his silver shock of hair somehow seeming to dominate the courtroom, and officially entered his plea of "not guilty".

The trial itself began on Thursday, September 7.

The courtroom was again packed with media, family members and friends of both Cooper and Snider, Fairview Health Complex staff and other Fairview residents. Others were curiosity seekers, some perpetual watchdogs whose lives revolved around the evolution of the daily dramas to be found in courtrooms. They were even reinforced by some who had been considered for jury duty but had not, for whatever reason, been chosen.

Abe Cooper, wearing a tan sport jacket, sat next to his lawyer, Larry Anderson at a table on one side of the courtroom. He seemed strangely at ease as he swiveled in his chair and swept his intense stare across the public benches. A security guard sat nearby. At another table to the left of the Cooper camp, sat Crown Prosecutor David Stilwell accompanied by the lead police investigator in the case, Wade Sparks.

Justice was about to be seen in action and for many in the room, including our family, for the first time. Some believed that the Crown represented the victim and the victim's family. However, our family had been educated in that matter during the build-up to the case, including the preliminary inquiry.

The police officers and the Crown lawyer had been helpful in providing information regarding the legal proceedings, especially for members of the family who were testifying as Crown witnesses. We quickly learned that our interests and the interests of our loved one were very much secondary to ensuring due process for Cooper. The Crown prosecutor represented the state so could not be an advocate for the victim. Nevertheless, we were reassured by Stilwell's meticulous, conscientious manner that he would do his best in prosecuting the case. We would now just have to trust the process.

The cramped observers, further agitated by their impatience for proceedings to begin, rose as one when Queen's Bench Justice Joanne Veit finally entered the courtroom.

The jury was a youngish one; the majority of members appeared to be in their thirties with perhaps only two or three more than fifty years old. They appeared uncertain and uneasy about what might be in store for them.

The judge informed them they were the real judges in this trial. They were, she said, the judges of the facts while she was the judge of the law. They were advised that they were not to talk about the case and were not to listen to, watch or read the news. The judge emphasized that the accused must be presumed innocent until he was proven guilty beyond a reasonable doubt.

In his opening statement, the Crown lawyer, David Stilwell, described his theory of the crime and named the 36 witnesses that he would be calling to testify. Stilwell outlined the history of strife in Fairview, the antipathy between Snider and Cooper, Cooper's growing frustration and desperation at the loss of income through the revocation of his hospital privileges, his blaming of Snider for his predicament, and his plot to remove his nemesis once and for all, starting by luring him to his office alone.

Throughout his opening remarks, Stilwell spoke in a quiet, methodical voice, directing his words to the jury a metre or two away from him. There were shuffles and sighs of frustration and exasperation in the public benches where nearly everyone had to lean forward to be able to hear the lawyer at all.

Defence lawyer Larry Anderson opened by cautioning the jury to be careful, noting that it was "easy to be swept up in" the Crown's story. He encouraged jurors to look below the surface at what was not so obvious, since maybe what they were hearing or were going to hear was "too obvious."

He told them that they would be hearing about the dysfunctional medical community in Fairview that wanted Cooper out of there since "he shone the spotlight on things".

Then he dropped his first bombshell. He said Snider had been seen alive since May 5, 1999, the day he supposedly disappeared.

Anderson further stunned the courtroom with his bold accusation that Snider was in fact capable of deliberately disappearing in order "to take his archrival down". He suggested that Snider had "spent much of his adult life out of touch with reality" and was so preoccupied with Cooper's lawsuit against him and the other doctors, he simply wanted it to go away.

Anderson then asked: "If you're guilty, does it make any sense that you're going to leave your car in plain view? Could this have been a set-up?"

Many reporters scrambled from the courtroom with cell phones already in hand to call in the dramatic twist right at the start of the trial. Part of Cooper's defence at least would be that rather than he being guilty of a truly heinous crime, it was Doug in fact who had devised a devilish scheme to bring him down.

The members of our family in court for the opening addresses were stunned and shocked that the defence seemed intent on taking a route that would inevitably involve the public discrediting of our loved one, the man who, after all, was the alleged victim in the case.

As witnesses in the trial, Doug's widow, Jean, and sons Darren and Doug, were not in court when the opening arguments were made. The Crown had asked witnesses, including them, to remain outside until after their testimony but we quickly filled them in on the defence position.

And soon we huddled together preparing a statement we knew the media would expect in light of the dramatic and unexpected thrust of the defence comments. Despite our obvious misgivings and distaste, we chose to inform the media that in order not to jeopardize the proceedings, our family would, unless under extenuating circumstances, refrain from commenting officially during the trial.

It fell to me to represent the family's position. Flanked by other family members, I read a prepared statement and responded to some questions. Guarded about speaking regarding the developments in the courtroom just prior to the statement, my comments were very brief.

But I was prepared. If I had been asked, I was ready to discount any suggestion that my brother could still be alive. My family and I, and likely the media representatives themselves knew that was impossible. The question was not raised.

Predictably and understandably, newspaper headlines the following day reflected the shock and dismay surrounding the defence theory. In bold print above a picture of Doug's smiling face, the broadsheet *Edmonton Journal*'s front-page headline asked:

Dr. Snider still alive?

The tabloid *Edmonton Sun* headline blared:

DOC TRIAL SHOCKER: Defence claims Fairview physician faked his own death.

The *Globe and Mail* headline, also on the front page, stated:

Defence raises startling theory in case of missing doctor: Lawyer suggests Alberta MD staged disappearance.

Our friends and family were appalled that anyone had had the audacity to pose such a supposition about the disappearance of our friend and loved one. We never guessed until then that defence tactics might involve calling into question the character and credibility of the man who was supposedly the victim in the astonishing case.

We felt we had suffered enough without this new outrage. But soon, inevitably, we realized our only hope was that once the court and the public heard the evidence, the real truth as to guilt and innocence would emerge.

As for the Cooper supporters, and there were some, a number may have truly believed the claim that Doug had conspired to disappear thus setting up Cooper, his longtime adversary, for the rap. They truly could not believe that Cooper was capable of murder.

But maybe, just maybe – at least the Snider camp hoped – some Cooper supporters also saw through the red herring ploy and recognized it as a desperate gimmick to plant the seeds of even the slightest doubt over the accused doctor's guilt.

The mood had very definitely changed on Day Two. This, everyone now realized, was going to be nasty. But somehow, as folk gathered in the courtroom that day, we remained aware that what really mattered was what the jury heard, understood and ultimately decided about guilt or innocence.

The starting point in that day's evidence was Abe Cooper's car, seemingly abandoned in haste at Edmonton International Airport. Royal Canadian Mounted Police Corporal Marc Barbey showed the court photographs of the car found in the airport parkade the morning after the evening Doug had received the phone call he'd told Jean was from Cooper.

The jury examined pictures of dried or drying blood in streams down the rear bumper and smeared on the tail lights of the vehicle. Bluntly, Barbey testified that the blood would have been in plain view to anyone walking past the car and happening to even glance in its direction.

Another key witness that day was Ken Landry, the local Fairview businessman who knew both Abe Cooper and Doug. Landry said that Cooper had spoken often with him about his lawsuit against the other town doctors. He also testified that on more than one occasion Doug had approached him to set up a meeting with Abe to try to settle the long on-going dispute. On three occasions, said the witness, he had spoken with Cooper in this regard.

But Cooper had always refused, Landry told the court, telling him to "tell Doug Snider to keep his money in the country because I'm going to get it all." Landry also stated that while Snider did want the lawsuit settled, he was also happily looking forward to retirement.

In another twist to what was already becoming a sensational trial, Landry spoke to the media after providing court with his testimony. He declared outright that there was no way that Doug Snider would have set the crime up and deliberately disappeared as the defence was suggesting in court.

Next day, with the comments having been reported on television, radio and in newspapers, defence lawyer Larry Anderson raised the post-testimony interview with the judge. The jury was not present in court as he made his point. He maintained that while there was concern that even though the jury had clearly been instructed not to watch or read media coverage of the case, there was a chance jury members may have heard Landry's comments, even though he had not testified to such during his time on the witness box.

The judge conceded people had a right to speak. The Crown suggested that this was an issue for the Bar to address later, pointing out that lawyers regularly give courthouse step interviews to media during a case.

After jury members entered the courtroom that morning, the judge reminded them that they were not to watch or read the news surrounding the case.

Chapter Seventeen

On the same day as the arguments on and regarding the appropriateness or otherwise of Landry's impromptu interview with the media, Dr. Paul Chung, another of the physicians whom Cooper was suing, was called to the witness box.

Early in his testimony, Chung was presented with a document allegedly signed by Doug Snider during his meeting with Cooper at the latter's office May 5, 1999.[19] The allegations made in the document were read to Chung who replied "False" to every statement. The document purported to be detrimental to Doug and amounted almost to a confession of sorts by the missing doctor to have plotted against Cooper. The dumbfounded Chung even asked at one point: "Where did these come from?"

He adamantly denied there had been any conspiracy against Cooper by Snider individually or as part of a group. Chung maintained that Cooper often refused to respond to night calls at the hospital.

Defence counsel Larry Anderson at one point suggested that Cooper had been left out of meetings at the hospital. Chung's dismissive replies and denials appeared to catch the defence off guard and worse, some of Chung's answers were proving decidedly derogatory to Cooper. Court adjourned early that afternoon due to technical difficulties in the courtroom and Chung's testimony was completed on the following Monday.

The drama heightened even further the following week when witnesses began building a picture for the jury of what had happened the night Doug disappeared. My sister-in-law, Jean Snider, casting a dignified but forlorn figure, gave her account of Doug's fateful call from Cooper, her conversation with her husband, and her actions and movements when he did not return from his meeting.

She had to endure a stressful cross-examination by defence counsel Anderson who dwelled greatly on Doug's history of substance abuse and his subsequent treatment in Atlanta in 1994. Jean, who had also worked as office manager for Doug's practice, testified that she was aware that his drinking had begun after he began practising medicine. She testified that Doug had the habit of drink-

---

[19] This document reappeared later in the trial when other persons named in it were called to testify.

ing when he was off call after a stressful day or week. He called it a "therapeutic drunk".

She described her husband as a worrier who wanted the long-running lawsuit issue to be resolved once and for all. She said that Doug felt it was "a groundless lawsuit". He had often said to her that he had tried his best and that he no longer knew what more he could do to resolve matters.

Jean swore that to her knowledge, Doug had used neither drugs nor alcohol since December 1994, when he had returned from treatment in the United States. She said he had frequently been monitored by the College of Physicians and Surgeons and that he never once had a positive laboratory result in his screening tests for drugs. Anderson however relentlessly continued on the issue of Doug's recovery, maintaining recovery meant more than not drinking. He raised questions about Doug's resentment.

If, at times, Anderson appeared to be trying to put words in her mouth, Jean replied: "I like my words better." Resolutely, she stuck with her position that her bottom line was that Doug had quit drinking, that he had enjoyed the twelve-step program and in his recovery, had actually enjoyed supporting and helping other alcoholics.

It was clear that Anderson's strategy was to discredit the witness and somehow establish any germ of his purported theory that Doug Snider had been in a state of mind to set Cooper up in some way.

Vi Landry, Doug's office nurse, testified that her employer had often spoken of the lawsuit, that he felt it was "totally unfounded" and that he had asked to speak with Cooper about it.

Vi recalled that since Dr. Cooper had refused to talk to him, Dr. Snider had found some encouragement in a casual street conversation with his antagonist at the end of April, relating to the sudden death of a patient. Since Dr. Snider was the medical examiner, Dr. Cooper had agreed to send on any relevant information. She told the court that at the time Dr. Snider had thought, "that was great" since Dr. Cooper was apparently willing to cooperate with him on this matter.

The nurse who had worked for Doug for 27 years testified that he had always worked very hard and had a busy practice. But she said she became aware that he had a problem with alcohol in 1992 but never saw him drunk or smelled alcohol on his breath. When pushed by the defence as to whether she observed cognitive impairment, agitation or paranoia, Vi Landry's reply was a straightforward "Never."

There was more pathos in the courtroom when Darren and Douglas Dean, were called to testify briefly on their relationship with their father. Each of them had given a blood sample to assist in identification of Doug's DNA in samples found in Cooper's office and in and on his car. Jean, having completed her testimony, was able to sit in the courtroom to hear her sons testify.

Another key witness on September 12 was Brenda Osowetski, Cooper's receptionist, who had been called by the police on the morning of May 6 to check his office.

The *Globe and Mail* newspaper was to report:

> What she found would have shocked just about anyone, though by her matter of fact testimony, one would have thought she had found just an upset garbage can.[20]

Osowetski reported finding pools of blood soaked into the carpet, chairs pushed around the office and a stool with a roll of duct tape with a blood smear, and a pad of paper on a desk. She also noted that the office blinds were closed. All of these were changes from the way she had left the office the previous evening, the night that Doug left his home allegedly to meet Cooper in the office.

She testified that Cooper had left the office at about 4 p.m. that day to prepare for his trip to Orlando, Florida the following morning.

There was one discrepancy between Brenda Osowetski's testimony and Jean Snider's testimony. Osowetski said that she had switched the office lights off when she had left that evening and had switched them back on when she returned the next morning with a police officer. Jean had said the lights were on the occasions she drove past the office overnight looking for any sign of her husband.

Cross-examined by Larry Anderson, Cooper's counsel, Osowetski told the still-jammed court that Cooper had been an excellent boss, fun to work with and said that she had never seen him lose his temper. Yes, she was aware that Cooper had lost his hospital privileges, and was suing Snider, Chung and Clarke. She said that Cooper had spoken of getting one of the three to come on side with him.

---

[20] "It was healing as usual day doctor disappeared," The *Globe and Mail*, September 13, 2000, A5.

Two young men who worked at Fast Gas in Fairview testified that Cooper had come in to fill up his car between 5 p.m. and 6 p.m. on the evening of May 5. The court was told that Cooper had also filled a gerry can with gas and they had noticed that there was grey carpeting in the trunk of the car when the can was placed in the trunk. The court was to hear later that that carpet was no longer in Cooper's car when it was seized at Edmonton Airport.

As the testimony went on and on, or reached uninteresting points, it was hard for the public jamming the benches not to allow their eyes to stray towards the accused. Whenever Cooper entered the courtroom accompanied by the ever-present guard, he himself was in the habit of scanning the courtroom. As his eyes darted to dart around the public benches, inevitably, his eyes would meet those of at least some of our family. On one occasion, he challenged one of the family: "It's pretty rude to stare like that."

His gaze, people had noticed, could be disconcerting and intimidating. If I, or others in the courtroom did stare at Cooper, it was at least in part an attempt to figure out what was going on in his mind. I often wondered how to understand the mind of a killer – the mind of one who had allegedly taken the life of my brother, and yet was able to sit in the courtroom next to his lawyer as if he was his assistant and not on trial himself.

How could this man, whom the court continued to address as Dr. Cooper and who was showing absolutely no empathy or concern for his victim, be a physician at all? I was hoping the jury was wondering exactly the same things.

Cooper's wife, Fay, faithfully attended the trial sitting in the front rows behind her husband, often accompanied by at least one or two female companions and at times by one or both of her sons. Occasionally, when a recess was called, Cooper would turn around to speak with her. In the corridors outside, in the waiting area and in the cafeteria, the Cooper family sat separate from other observers.

While we felt compassion for the Cooper family's situation, there was no way of telling what was going through their minds or what they knew or believed to be the truth. There was no communication between our two families.

Evidence photos above. Blood on the floor of Dr. Abe Cooper's office. Blood on bumper of Abe Cooper's car. Reprinted from Edmonton Journal newspaper, September 30, 2000.

Chapter Eighteen

On September 13, witnesses included a number of RCMP officers who had been involved in the case.

They testified how their investigation had revealed a trail of blood from the scene of the alleged crime, Cooper's office, to his car later found in the parkade at the Edmonton International Airport, and on his clothes that he was carrying in a bag on his return to Edmonton from Florida. They recalled that early in the morning following his meeting with Snider, Cooper had caught a flight out of Edmonton in order to attend a conference in Orlando, Florida.

Royal Canadian Mounted Police Corporal Craig Bentley Smith told how he had collected blood samples from the car's license plate and from its trunk. And grimly, he reported finding "up to one-quarter inch of blood in the wheel well and a fair bit of blood in the trunk itself".[21] Smith said he also collected hair samples from the base of the trunk lid and the trunk latch.

This was the day that our father, George Schattschneider, attended the trial for the first time. He was surrounded by family members, each of us deeply concerned about how he would cope with the court experience in general, and in particular, with the graphic nature of the evidence.

Our family elder, who was 89 years of age at the time, was determined that he would return. Dad said he found it easier to be with the family than wait alone at home for news every day, and he felt Doug would have wanted him to be there.

Most days, there were at least ten members of our family in attendance. Other extended family members and friends also came regularly to listen to the proceedings. We needed to be there for Doug and for each other as we waited for justice to unfold. Daena arrived from Australia in time for the last two weeks of the trial.

A key piece of evidence was a document that had been turned over to police on May 25 by Peter Royal, lawyer from the office of Cooper's civil lawyer, Gary Romanchuk. Cooper's wife, Fay Cooper, had delivered the written statement now under scrutiny to Romanchuk's office on the morning following Doug's disappearance.

---

[21] According to testimony by a DNA expert later in the trial, the blood samples were confirmed by DNA analysis to be Doug's blood. The blood on Cooper's clothes, the blood on the shoes he was still wearing when he got off the plane and the back pocket of his pants, was also determined to be Doug's. Stains on Cooper's shirt were established to be a mixture of Cooper's own and Doug's blood.

Correspondence from Romanchuk to Cooper had been found in Cooper's office during the police investigation. It included a bill for his legal fees and a copy of the judgement in Cooper's final appeal regarding his hospital privileges. Lawyer Romanchuk was originally scheduled as a Crown witness. Instead he submitted a written statement to the court rather than make a personal appearance. No reason for that change was given, at least in open court.

The document under scrutiny was the supposed "confession" by Doug. For the purposes of the trial the handwritten version – in Doug's own hand – was entered as Exhibit No. 26, and then a typewritten copy was entered as Exhibit No. 27. Both, it appeared, had been signed by Doug and were dated May 5, 1999, the very night he met with Abe Cooper and didn't return home.

The defence claimed that Doug had written the statement voluntarily. The Crown argued that Doug had been forced into writing the handwritten version as he was being held captive by Cooper.

The statement, almost but tellingly not quite identical in both versions, opens with a declaration that in order to bring closure to the dispute between Cooper and Chung, Clarke and himself, Snider agreed to testify at a trial admitting there had been a conspiracy against Cooper.

If, as the jury was to decide later, he wrote the so-called confession under threat and under the glare of Cooper that fateful night, it is hard to contemplate the terror Doug faced.

There are 25 paragraphs in the statement and thus it would have taken some considerable time to write. It is, of course, impossible to know what must have been going through Doug's mind as he wrote in shaky but totally legible hand.

Did he know his life was at risk?

Did he think he would be released alive by writing it and signing it?

Was he simply buying time and looking for an opportunity to escape?

It is chilling to think of the awful scene in Abe Cooper's office that night.

The statement's opening paragraphs read:

> This is to certify I have read the statement of claim between A. Cooper and Chung-Snider-Clarke and that the claims in this statement are true and correct.

I agree to testify at trial and that testimony will include but not be limited to:

1. Specific dates, times and places when Chung, Clarke and myself met to discuss specific strategies to attack Cooper.
2. Specific fabrications which we all agreed to promulgate;
3. That Chung brought groundless allegations, about Cooper, to the hospital administer[22] D. Magnusson, and that he refused to put these things in writing i.e. he knew they were illegal according to the hospital staff bylaws.
4. Chung, Clarke and myself encouraged D. Magnusson to take action on these allegations even though they were groundless, improper and illegal.
5. Chung, Clarke and myself held a meeting unknown to Cooper to review complaints against Cooper and then wrote a letter to the Hospital Board denouncing Cooper.
6. Clarke made false allegations to Dr. Fraser to attack Cooper.
7. D. Makarenko, D. Magnusson and other members of the Fairview Hospital Board were aware of and supported our efforts to attack Cooper in order to cover up longstanding and ongoing problems in the medical staff.
8. Our overall goal was to force Cooper to leave Fairview to prevent exposure of internal problems and to gain the revenue from his considerable practice.
9. We all encouraged L. Westin to lodge a complaint against Cooper,[23] ... and to deliberately lie about Cooper's actions on the case.
10. We agreed to deny Cooper's patients outpatient services, to which they were entitled, in order to destroy his reputation and his practice(...).[24]
11. We did everything we could to ensure Cooper would suffer large legal expenses.
12. We encouraged D. Magnusson to complain to the College of Physicians and Surgeons regarding Cooper's chelation practice.
13. We encouraged D. Magnusson to deliberately lie about Cooper's hospital privileges (flexible sigmoidoscopy) in order to aggravate Cooper.
14. We collectively and individually made statements that we knew would aggravate Cooper.
15. We collectively and individually refused to work with Cooper in order to destroy his practice. We threatened to resign if Cooper was not terminated.

---

[22] Handwritten version, "administrator"

[23] The hand written copy shows an obvious correction presumably by Snider to the spelling of the patient's name. That name is omitted in this publication for purposes of confidentiality.

[24] Patient's names omitted.

16. I wrote a letter to the Fairview Post to aggravate Cooper. I knew that letter contained deliberate lies.

17. I have read the transcript of Cooper's Hospital Appeal Board Hearing, Nov. '97 and I will testify that D. Magnusson, D Makarenko, G. Northam and B. Strom were all privy to our strategic plans to force Cooper to leave Fairview and that they fully supported us in order to cover up ongoing internal problems.

18. We encouraged the Fairview Hospital Board and the Mistahia Health Authority to work in secrecy in order to prevent the public from knowing the truth.

19. This is to certify I have read the statement of claim between Cooper and Mistahia Health Authority and that the claims in that statement are true and correct.

20. I will testify that Cooper's privileges were improperly and illegally terminated at the urging of Chung, Clarke and myself.

21. D. Makarenko urged the board to terminate Cooper's privileges on the pretext he refused to sign the Code of Conduct when in fact he had not been given the document to sign. This was known to the members of the Fairview Hospital Board, Staples, Chung, Clarke and myself.

22. We encouraged the Fairview Hospital Board to ignore all of Cooper's legitimate complaints and we urged the board to take action against Cooper for bringing these complaints forward.

The handwritten version is signed and dated at this point by Doug. The typed version continues:

23. Clarke refused to reinstate Cooper on the ER (Emergency Room) call roster despite the ruling of the Hospital Appeal Board in June 95. We were all aware of this and approved of it.

In conclusion, the typed version states:

In return for my testimony outlined above and such other facts that may come to light at trial I will receive immunity from any judgement against me by Dr. Cooper as I have discussed with Dr. Cooper.[25]

Doug's signature follows. The 23 itemized statements in the document matched the claims in Cooper's lawsuit against the Fairview doctors.

Three copies of the document had been received at the lawyer's office. Tim McLean, an RCMP document examiner, testified that except for one page of one version, the typed pages were photocopies. He said the handwritten copy did not include item #23 and a final declaration on the typewritten copy that stated that Snider

---

[25] Photocopy of typewritten document attached as an Appendix to Judge Maher's summation of the Preliminary Inquiry, Criminal Division of the Provincial Court of Alberta. September 20, 1999. Document was submitted as Exhibit #27 for the trial.

would receive immunity from any judgment against him in return for his testimony.

McLean testified that the handwriting of the handwritten copy matched samples of Snider's writing. The documents were apparently signed by Snider, but McLean could not be certain that another signature on the typewritten copies – above a line denoted 'witness signature' – that looked like Cooper MD was actually that of Cooper.

McLean testified that at least the last page of the handwritten document came from the pad of paper found in Cooper's office and that the typewritten versions had been typed on one of the two typewriters seized from Cooper's office.

In the preliminary inquiry, McLean had also reported that when examining the ribbons and daisy wheel of the typewriters, he had found the words: "This is the day that Teddy Bears have their picnic." That information was not included in his trial testimony.

McLean testified there was evidence that Cooper had apparently prepared the documents prior to his meeting with Snider. The Crown's position was that when Snider met Cooper, he had been confined and then forced by Cooper to sign these documents.

Chapter Nineteen

The alleged confession by Doug became the focus of the testimony of persons named in the document. Each witness adamantly denied the truth of the statements. Dr. Chung, the first witness to testify regarding the truth of the document, had denied that there was a conspiracy and offered further information regarding Cooper's attitude and behavior.

When the Crown was about to call its next witnesses in this regard, the defence requested time on September 14 to discuss the admissibility of certain evidence.

Our family, having listened to the defence's seemingly-calculated demeaning of Doug's character, listened again as Anderson said the court was "entering an area of evidence fraught with potential concerns... I have to know the Crown's position before I can structure my cross-examination." Anderson suggested that the Crown's approach was different from that in the preliminary hearing.

In fact, it was the defence's position that had changed. Tom Engel, Cooper's lawyer in the preliminary inquiry, had never at any point claimed that Doug was still alive. Instead, his line of questioning had seemed to be looking for evidence that Doug was violent and that Cooper was acting in self-defense.

Apparently, in the time interval between the preliminary inquiry and the trial, the defence learned that in May 1999, two British Columbia truck drivers had reported to the police that they might have seen the missing doctor at a truck stop. This report gave the defendant and his lawyer an opportunity to pursue another angle on the case.

Anderson had taken over the case only weeks before the trial began. He now stated: "The Crown is calling witnesses to defend against opinion evidence given on an issue ... this is not a trial on conspiracy ... there is potential for misuse of evidence." He was concerned, he said, about evidence of "bad character".

So the jury was sent home while the lawyers presented their respective arguments to the judge relating to the admissibility of evidence concerning Cooper's character and motive. The Crown argued that evidence relating to Cooper and the events at the Fairview Hospital Complex prior to the murder were relevant as they applied to Cooper's motive. Those motives included perceptions, beliefs, values and emotions manifested in short and long-term behavior.

The judge clarified that motive was admissible but general bad character was not. However, Stilwell argued that what he firmly maintained was Cooper's vindictive conduct ought to be admissible, adding that the defence is not entitled to a "sanitized version" of the evidence.

Judge Veit identified two exceptions when evidence of bad character is allowed: First, when the accused challenges the character of the victim, the Crown had a right to rehabilitate the victim's character simply as a matter of fairness; and secondly, when the evidence has a definable purpose.

The defence maintained that the Crown was the first to enter character evidence about Snider as it related to his daily routine and lifestyle. Larry Anderson stated: "The defence has not sought to produce evidence that Snider is a bad person in a moral sense ... he has a long-standing alcohol problem ... carrying with it all kinds of psychological problems ... he covers things up."

He further argued that the "rosy picture sought to be portrayed by the Crown is not accurate. In fact these aspects of Snider's life ... are not as stated to be ... have been exposed ... he resents having been exposed ... have far more to do with the way he would want to get away ... the document saves his family and ends the lawsuit."[26]

The defence's arguments seemed to be reflections of Cooper's ongoing attitude toward and accusations against Doug. Our family wondered whether the judge and the jury would recognize these claims as continuing evidence of Cooper's vindictiveness.

In order to assist in making a ruling on the debate of what should or should not be admissible, the Crown Stilwell proposed the judge review a binder of essential documents concerning Cooper and the events at the Fairview Health Complex from November 1992 to March 23, 1994.

Stilwell had flagged information in these documents as follows:
F for *false* statements.

A for *absence of malice* on the part of Snider toward the accused (Cooper).

D for *disruptive/defiant* behavior of Cooper which had been the cause of the removal of his hospital privileges.

---

[26] The truth is that when Doug was a practising alcoholic, he did deny or minimize the extent of his drinking problem. However, in all other aspects of his life, he was a naturally open person and therefore vulnerable.

And finally, V for *vindictiveness* shown towards his colleagues by Cooper.

In his review of the documents, Stilwell pointed out a pattern of Cooper's perception of any challenge to his behavior as a personal attack to which he would respond with a counter attack ... "not a defence, but a counter-attack," the prosecutor noted. An example was a documented statement made by Cooper during the earlier reviews of his conduct at the hospital. It read: "They complained about me, I'll complain about them."

Stilwell vehemently argued that the heart of the whole case was the relationship between the two men, noting Snider's efforts had been concentrated on reconciliation while Cooper's approach had been one of counter attack.

The court adjourned in order for Judge Viet to review the documents and make a decision regarding admissibility.

When court reconvened on Tuesday, September 19, the judge rendered her decision that information from the documents that were flagged as *false* and information that demonstrated Snider's *absence of malice* toward Cooper would be admissible. But she ruled that information that demonstrated Cooper's *defiance* and *vindictiveness* was inadmissible stating that this information was more prejudicial than probative. In effect, the judge was ensuring the law was applied in such a way as not to be prejudiced against the accused through bad character evidence.

It was a huge blow to our family and most members of the health care community in Fairview who were in court. We knew the magnitude of Cooper's disruptive behavior and now most of the telling evidence in that pivotally historic matter would not be heard.

All we could do was seek possible consolation in the hope that if the law had been followed so meticulously in order to ensure that Cooper had a fair trial, surely then there would be no grounds for any appeal of any conviction.

Chapter Twenty

The trial proper resumed. The Crown's David Stilwell explained he would be advising his witnesses to refrain from any comments that might cast a shadow on Cooper's character.

Key witness Dennis Magnusson[27], a former administrator at Fairview Health Complex during much of Cooper's tenure there, testified at length on the difficulties during his term in the position. Magnusson denied any truth in the statements contained in Doug's alleged confession adding at one point that "all complaints were reviewed on more than one occasion." He spoke of how he had tried to bring order to the Fairview Health Complex and of how the series of events leading to Cooper's loss of privileges were reviewed.

Under cross-examination by Larry Anderson, Magnusson testified that Cooper wasn't a team player. "At the beginning, we had to get everyone to work together... he had to decide to come on side, that's why we had a code of conduct," he said. Magnusson stressed that Cooper had been given "more than ample opportunity to sign the code" but when he refused to do so, his hospital privileges had not been renewed.

Magnusson testified that at its meeting on March 23, 1994, the hospital board was "gravely concerned ... and left with no choice but to not reappoint Cooper in the interest of the hospital and of serving the community".

The defence focused on Cooper's accusations of "bad medicine" at the Fairview Hospital and his request to Magnusson to do something about it. Anderson grilled Magnusson on Doug's alcohol problem and the witness told court he had first become aware of the doctor's problem in the spring of 1993. But Magnusson seemed to come to Doug's defence when he emphasized that Snider was frustrated with the situation, "was very sincere about resolving problems and wanted to work together ... to settle things ... to move on."

When Anderson suggested that "he (Snider) wanted to cover this mess up", Magnusson's reply was: "I don't think so ... he wanted to move on ... he was frustrated with going into the past."

---

[27] Note that there are references to two people with a similar name with a slightly different spelling in this story. Dennis Magnusson, witness at the trial, was the former hospital administrator in Fairview. Hazel Magnussen, author of this book, is the younger sister of Doug Snider sr., the murder victim.

It was a direct reference to complaints by Cooper regarding past grievances. Magnusson testified that when he learned of Snider's drinking problem, he chose to monitor the situation, noted that Snider worked hard, was under a lot of stress and "needed understanding and support, not criticism".

To most, the trial now seemed to be dragging.

The testimony of Magnusson, who had taken time off from his administrative position in Abbotsford, B.C., had been delayed because of the legal debate about admissibility of evidence. Now involved in lengthy testimony, he was beginning to show signs of fatigue as the defence continued to push for any information that would tarnish Doug more than Cooper.

The defence spent some time referring to a discharge summary of Doug's treatment for his alcoholism in the Atlanta treatment center. Reading short excerpts from the summary describing Doug's behavior early in his treatment, Anderson questioned Magnusson as to whether he had observed these behaviors.

Magnusson referred back to Snider's frustration regarding the situation with Cooper, but Anderson continued to focus on "Snider's mood swings, anxiety, paranoia and obsessive thinking." He did not ask for comments on Doug's completion of treatment and successful return to practice. Magnusson had already left the community on Doug's return.

Magnusson, however, did testify that Snider called him in early 1995 to talk about the ongoing problems in Fairview so as "to get things in context" and wondering who would provide leadership in resolving the issues.

There was another interruption in the trial when the Crown called for another voir dire (a legal discussion held without the jury being present) after Anderson had been questioning Magnusson for hours about the details of Cooper's past grievances. Stilwell referred to the "strategic possibility to descend into the quagmire of vindictiveness ... any defence lawyer could not avoid opening up vindictiveness ... Mr. Anderson has been forced into a quagmire..."

Again the jury was sent home while discussion this time focused on the admissibility of evidence that pointed to Cooper's vindictiveness towards Snider. Cooper's letter of fourteen points was considered. The Crown's Stilwell described these points as being "to a large degree, retaliation" and hard evidence of Cooper's actual vindictiveness. The defence argued that this information would lead the jury into the quagmire of the conspiracy, was therefore considered more prejudicial than probative, and the judge ruled it would not advance the case.

Observers who thought themselves well versed in the reality of the drawn out affair in Fairview were convinced that the jury would now only be getting glimpses of an extremely multi-faceted situation. The public was hearing even less of the story. And those courtroom observers could be heard during the recesses discussing the proceedings and wondering aloud who really was on trial in the case. At least one skeptic was overheard to express concern that by now the jury may have become confused as to who was the victim and who was the accused.

Meanwhile, the defence continued to cast Cooper as the victim of injustice, reiterating Cooper's complaints that had already been reviewed at length in previous legal proceedings. During the preliminary inquiry just over one year earlier, considerable time had also been spent reviewing Cooper's grievances and Doug's history of alcoholism. Some had wondered at that time how these were relevant to the charges against Cooper.

However, it was evident in Judge Maher's summation of the preliminary inquiry that the information had been useful in understanding Cooper's behavior and attitude toward Doug, and Cooper's supposed motive for killing him. The judge stated:

> There are, however, three areas of evidence from which, in my view, an inference can be drawn that the accused intended to kill Dr. Snider, that the killing was planned and deliberate, and that it occurred while Dr. Snider was being confined.

On the question of motive, Judge Maher sated:

> It goes without saying that motive, if it exists, is capable of being used to draw an inference of an intention to kill as well as an inference that the killing was planned and deliberate.

> The evidence suggests that the accused had three strong, separate, and discernible motives to kill Dr. Snider, although they are admittedly intertwined. Firstly the accused had extensive personal grievances as evidenced by the claims made by him in the lawsuit and throughout the hospital privileges litigation. Rightly or wrongly, accurately or inaccurately, justifiably or not, legitimate or coloured, and it matters not for this purpose, there is abundant evidence that in the accused's mind, he was an aggrieved victim, wholly or partly because of Dr. Snider and as a result of Dr. Snider's conduct. Sec-

ondly, there is evidence of dislike and enmity, bordering on hatred by the accused towards Dr. Snider. Thirdly, Dr. Snider was seen by the accused, as evidenced by the lawsuit, as a barrier to the accused's past and current financial benefit. The removal of Dr. Snider would be one less roadblock to reinstatement of the accused's hospital privileges.

Moreover, there is evidence from which it could be inferred that those motives intensified shortly before the killing. The outstanding litigation had been building.

Less than two months before the killing, the accused lost his case of judicial review with respect to his hospital privileges. This loss was the third of the hierarchy of forums where the accused sought a remedy to regain those privileges. He had lost at every level, and lost for the same reasons. Each tribunal had indicated that it was not an issue of who was to blame, who was correct, what was right, or if there were procedural fairness. Those were the battlegrounds on which the accused staked his claim. Each time he was told that those were not where the fight would be determined. The battlegrounds on which the issue was resolved was that of practicality, not principle. However, the last lost battle was at considerable financial cost to the accused.[28]

At the trial, Judge Veit did not accept the Crown's arguments that Cooper's defiant, disruptive behavior and vindictiveness was important evidence of his motive for killing Doug and ought to be admissible. The defence was permitted to continue to focus on how Cooper had been wronged despite the fact that the preliminary hearing's Judge Maher had stressed that the issue for the trial clearly was not who was right or who was wrong.

Next to take the witness stand was Dr. John Clarke. Clarke, one of the three physicians named in the infamous Fairview lawsuit, had testified at the various earlier hearings even though he had left the town some years before.

Clarke began his testimony with an overview of the history of complaints made by Cooper and of the various reviews of those concerns. He adamantly denied the veracity of the statements in the document allegedly signed by Doug voluntarily according to the defence and under duress according to the Crown.

In reference to past issues relating to call schedules and assistance in surgery at Fairview Hospital, Clarke said that when the working situation with Cooper had become intolerable, he had stopped assisting Cooper in elective surgery. Clarke said that despite

---

[28] Transcript of Preliminary Inquiry, Regina vs. Cooper, Criminal Division of the Provincial Court of Alberta, September 20th, 1999, p.1095-1097.

Cooper's attempt to blame him for his problems, Clarke always stressed that he was available for emergencies.

In cross-examination, Anderson referred to notes taken by Doug during the examination for discovery in a hearing into the lawsuit just prior to his disappearance and death. Doug had made reminders to himself in anticipation of his own examination. Defence counsel Anderson particularly noted Doug's statement that "Clarke said we have to follow the bylaws." The inference seemed to be that Clarke had coached Doug as to how to testify.

Clarke retorted that it was his duty to follow the bylaws and that this was an appropriate answer and was not an excuse. When asked about his, and Snider's attitude towards the lawsuit, Clarke replied simply: "We had nothing to hide."

Anderson switched the questioning to Clarke's knowledge of Snider's alcoholism. Clarke testified that he first became aware of Snider's drinking in 1993 and that he had supported Snider in getting assistance for his problem. He told court that Snider had gone for treatment in Atlanta voluntarily and that on his return, Snider had regularly attended Alcoholics Anonymous meetings.

Clarke said that in his conversation with Snider on the day of the discovery hearing, Snider had told him that he was happy he had gone for treatment, but was frustrated that his freedom had been taken away while involved in the process.

Anderson shifted the questioning back and forth between Doug's alcoholism and Cooper's grievances with Clarke. At one point, Clarke pointed out to Anderson that he was confusing the circumstances of two separate clinical cases.

Clarke responded throughout with short, clear answers. Anderson appeared confrontational, apparently trying to unnerve Clarke and discredit his testimony. At one point, the lawyer even charged: "You're making things up as you go along."

Clarke replied politely and confidently: "I disagree with you."

Meanwhile, other Crown witnesses who were part of the Fairview Hospital experience and who had testified at previous hearings regarding Dr. Cooper's behavior and his grievances against them, continued to wait in the court waiting room for their turn to testify. They knew the story well and patiently stood by prepared to tell what they were allowed to tell in order to shed light on the tragedy that continued to haunt them.

Another hospital witness, Lisa Westin, who had been a nursing supervisor at the Fairview Hospital, spoke of an incident that occurred at the hospital in 1996, after Dr. Cooper had lost his hospital privileges but had continued his practice in the community.

Westin told how a patient of Dr. Cooper was sent to the hospital where she was admitted under the care of Dr. Snider, the on-call physician. Dr. Cooper insisted that he did not want the patient treated by Dr. Snider, that he wanted only for her to have tests and then to return to his clinic.

Westin said the patient was grey and clammy and had a slow pulse and shortness of breath, so she asked Dr. Cooper to reconsider his request and plan.

According to Westin, Dr. Cooper then suggested sending the patient to Grande Prairie Hospital. But because the patient was in need of treatment, Westin called Dr. Snider who ordered tests and treatment for the patient.

When Dr. Cooper arrived shortly afterwards, said Westin, he demanded that she take out the patient's intravenous and that he was having a friend pick her up. Westin testified she refused because the patient's condition was unstable. Eventually the patient's condition was stabilized.

Those involved in the Fairview saga, or at least with some insight into it, hoped the judge and jury had latched onto what they saw as a focal, underlying issue in the case – a fight over control of patients rather than consideration for the patient's best interests.

Did it not encapsulate the whole issue?

Was this incident not an example of Dr. Cooper's disruptive behavior that jeopardized patient care by intimidating nursing staff to obey his orders?

Another witness on what was a significant day was Doreen Makarenko, chairperson of the Fairview Hospital Board from 1992 until 1994. She testified that the Board had always been desperate to normalize relations during the conflict and to protect patient care in the community. But in answer to prosecutor Stilwell she admitted: "We were simply a mess. We had to look to the safety of our staff. Our staff were fearful. We were very close to being paralyzed."

Stilwell pointedly asked Makarenko whether there had ever been a conspiracy to run Dr. Cooper out of town and so, at the same time, cover up the problems in the health community.

"That was the last thing we wanted to happen," Makarenko insisted in her answer. "We were always short of doctors in Fairview. Why should we cover up the problems? Everybody in the province knew about them."

Even in a case that was continuing to shock court officers and onlookers alike through its surprises and the nature of its evidence, September 25 – the day the defence began to present its case – stands out as a unique day.

Defence lawyer Larry Anderson called two West coast truckers to testify. With many of our family in attendance, the defence offered another element to the case, one that it hoped would throw reasonable doubt on Cooper's guilt – even on the fact that Doug Snider was dead at all.

The truckers Sylvie Loiseau and Terry Anderson said they had gone to police May 11 after seeing a black and white picture of Dr. Doug Snider come up on the television screen at the motel room they were occupying. They thought they recognized him as a man they had met the previous night.

The truckers testified they had stopped for a coffee in Golden, a bustling resort and lumber town in the B.C. Rockies, three hours west of Calgary on the Trans Canada Highway, at around 10 p.m. on May 10, 1999. During their pit stop, they had gotten into conversation with a friendly, well-dressed and seemingly well-educated man sitting alone at the next table.

They remembered that he was slightly overweight, was wearing khaki or beige pants, a short-sleeved striped shirt and had graying blonde hair. During their chat, the man said that he had traveled from Cranbrook in southeastern B.C. but did not mention in which direction he was headed. He seemed to know something of trucks and the industry and especially the transportation of gases such as oxygen, they testified.

The witness, Terry Anderson wrote in a statement that the man with whom they talked was "very composed, very calm. He had nice, clean soft hands that looked well groomed."

When cross examining the witnesses, Prosecutor Stilwell concentrated on the brevity of two crucial elements – first the length of the encounter with the mystery man in the coffee shop, and in the duration of the news item on television. Could they be sure the man was Snider?

Neither of them could be.

Also in court that day, two other doctors gave evidence that there had been a history of incidents at the Fairview Hospital long before the arrival of Abe Cooper in 1989.

Doctors Dietrich Wittel and George Stewart-Hunter testified there had been fistfights, erratic behaviour, sloppy care, threats and violence. Although the hospital board, the administrators, and the Alberta College of Physicians had been informed of the irregularities and thus were aware of them, no steps had been taken to deal with the problems.

Wittel even went further in personal remarks about Doug. Testifying he had arrived in Fairview in 1979, he said he had never trusted Snider and had even grown frightened of him because of his "irrational" behaviour and his "violent mood swings". In further shock testimony, he even went as far as to describe Doug as brutal, violent and deceitful.

Cross-examined by Stilwell, however, Wittel oddly and significantly was completely unable to explain why he thought Snider was a violent man, and admitted that the man he had criticized as such had never once lain a hand on him.

The waiting room outside the courtroom was crowded as usual on Thursday, September 28, as media, members of both the Snider and Cooper families, and other courtroom observers waited for it to open.

By now, the tension was almost unbearable. It was a tension born and built by defence counsel Anderson hammering away at crown witnesses attempting to portray his client as a victim of unfair treatment at the Fairview Hospital Complex, and to portray Doug, the physician who had allegedly been killed by Cooper, as a villain who had faked his own death in order to bring Cooper down.

Now everyone wondered what more was in store during the testimony of defence witnesses.

Anderson had staked a lot of his case on the truck drivers' testimony that they thought they might have seen Dr. Snider at a truck stop in B.C. after his disappearance. The testimony, he obviously hoped, would be seen by some of the jury at least as reasonable doubt that Snider was dead. And if he wasn't dead, how could Cooper be guilty of killing him?

The truckers of course had also testified that the glimpse of Doug's picture that they had seen on television was a fleeting one. When later shown another photo of Doug, they said that the face was not that of the man to whom they had spoken. They had, however, requested an original copy of the picture other than a faxed copy, but had not received one. The defence was now blaming police for inadequate follow up procedures.

The day began with yet another strange development. Without the jury present, the Crown's Stilwell suggested that he might have to apply for an adjournment.

Stilwell said he might have to step down as Crown counsel in order to testify himself as to his part in the investigation and the procedural follow-up to the truckers' alleged sightings of Snider. Stilwell stressed that the jury should not be led to believe that there was evidence that had not been presented. "There can be no implications that there have been sightings that have not been followed up," he said.

And he appealed further to the judge: "I will ask you to charge the jury that it (the sighting by the truck drivers) was useless evidence ... that neither I nor the police have neglected to follow up fully any reported sighting of Dr. Snider... that any speculation of the police investigation should not go to jury."

Following the discussion between the lawyers and the judge and further deliberation, the decision was made to carry on.

The waiting area outside the courtroom was buzzing about another matter that day. The day before, the *Edmonton Journal* had reported that the accused Cooper by now had a website and many present that Thursday had apparently already checked it out. The site contained much about Cooper's old grievances plus apparently new allegations of perjury by hospital personnel and police at his bail hearing, and complaints of mistreatment by the justice system.

It included accusations against Doug, even quoting a physician who served on a monitoring committee for the College of Physicians and Surgeons, and who was due to testify later as an expert witness for the defence. On his site, Dr. Cooper openly appealed to the public for assistance to free him and urged people to write to the Minister of Justice on his behalf.

Speculation was rife. How could he even dare to make these claims while the trial was in progress? Would the matter be raised in court? And the big question: Would Cooper take the stand in his own defence?

The previous few days in court had been hard on our family, as we were forced to listen to scathing accusations against our loved one that we knew were untrue.

The defence had called Barry Oliver, owner of a Fairview bar, to testify that he had seen Doug come to his bar every few months for off track betting and to drink soda, water or beer. We had certainly seen no evidence of his drinking alcohol and found the testimony confusing and troublesome. Had Doug actually drunk the beer he was said to have purchased? No one knew for sure. The testimony had been called as a result of the work of a private detective hired by Cooper to find evidence against Doug.

Inevitably, the media coverage during these days reflected the testimony and cast Doug as the troubled, desperate man portrayed by the defence. Our family felt that we were all being violated and victimized yet again.

Our family worried that those who scanned only the headlines and didn't bother to read the fine print would surely be confused as to what was happening in the trial and what was the real story. Some members of the public hanging around the court were heard to comment that they truly believed that "Snider had staged his own death".

What was the jury thinking? The trial was not yet over and there were still more accusations to come.

Dr. William James Mayhew was called to testify as an expert witness for the defence. Larry Anderson stated that he was "seeking to illicit information from Dr. Mayhew as expert witness regarding alcoholism and alcohol and addictions in the medical community."

Mayhew, a family physician in Calgary, Alberta and a medical classmate of Doug's, was at the time of the trial the chair of the Physicians Continuing Care Committee of the College of Physicians and Surgeons of Alberta. The committee oversaw the recovery contracts with licensed physicians who had been impaired by drugs, alcohol or mental illness. In this capacity, Dr.Mayhew's involvement with Doug was related to his aftercare following his treatment in Atlanta.

While Mayhew was not there to testify directly against Doug or to speak regarding his recovery, the defence did raise questions that related specifically to Doug's situation. As in his cross-examination of Crown witnesses regarding Doug's alcoholism, it was apparent that Anderson had knowledge of the disease and his probing questions zeroed in on certain aspects of alcoholism rehabilitation.

At one point, Anderson asked Mayhew if obsessive thinking was a characteristic of an alcoholic. Mayhew's reply was that it was also a characteristic of a successful physician... and then added "or lawyer".

This prompted laughter from some in the courtroom. Some of us knew how committed Doug was to ensuring that his patients were adequately cared for, a characteristic that some had said was bordering on obsessive.

Anderson probed further with questions relating to Doug's apparent resentments and quoted again from Doug's private notebook. The notebook that the defence was using as evidence against Doug had in fact been given to the police as a sample of Doug's handwriting. But through the legal process, it had ended up in the hands of the defence. The defence was now using some of the statements to denigrate or decry my brother.

There were many other statements in the book expressing Doug's concern that the people in Fairview were the losers, as local physicians were constantly having to close their offices in order to deal with Cooper's ongoing grievances. And, almost in a show of compassion towards Cooper himself, Doug wondered what kind of upbringing his long time adversary had had. The defence made no reference to these and other notebook entries.

Doug's resentment regarding his treatment and the ongoing dealings with Cooper was related to the fact that while he had undergone monitoring for his substance abuse, Cooper was never held accountable for his disruptive behavior.

Instead, Doug had always perceived, Cooper continued to harass the community and his colleagues through litigations that gave him a forum to continue to cast blame on others rather than ever take responsibility for his own actions. It seemed Cooper's pattern of counter attack was continuing now in the murder trial.

Anderson also read excerpts from Doug's discharge treatment summary and later asked for the summary to be submitted as evidence. The judge ruled it inadmissible noting that it was a complex document and could well be subject to misinterpretation. In fact, it had already been open to misinterpretation when it was used by the defence as a reference in its cross examination of some witnesses.

Judge Veit did, however, admit the rehabilitation contract that Doug had signed on the completion of his treatment.

So once again observers were left to wonder just how far Anderson would go to get further support for his theory? It remained uncertain at the end of that eventful Thursday whether there would be further defence witnesses.

When the court reconvened on Friday, September 29, the defence indicated that he had no further witnesses. So there it was, at last. Dr. Abraham Cooper would not be taking the stand. The jury was advised that the evidence was now in, and court would adjourn until Monday when they would hear closing arguments.

In all, the jury had heard from 38 witnesses and viewed 55 exhibits including photos and documents.

Chapter Twenty-one

The courtroom was filled to capacity on the morning of Monday, October 2. The proceedings were moving into their climactic moments. People who had been attending the trial wanted to be sure to hear the closing arguments of the lawyers in a trial that was now entering its fifth week.

Larry Anderson, the defence lawyer, began with an appeal to the jury to recognize the pressure he was feeling. He said: "For better or for worse, I've done what I could. How am I going to feel if I go out on a bender? How would I feel? When a person is under pressure, he lets himself down."

And then he applied these thoughts to Doug. In the process, our family was convinced the lawyer's remarks bordered on libel of a dead man who was unable to defend himself. Anderson outlined a picture of Doug's downward spiral into decline and despair over his dealings with Cooper – a collapse that allegedly led Doug into the bizarre course of action of maliciously creating his own disappearance and death so as to set up Abe Cooper with criminal charges.

Bewildered and exasperated, we could only listen in stunned silence as Anderson laid out a case designed to introduce reasonable doubt into the jury's thinking process. In doing so, Anderson branded Doug as a wicked, obsessed and scheming drunk set on fabricating a crime that would frame Cooper.

Anderson, picking voraciously at Doug's alcoholism, described Doug as being "plagued by demons". And in yet another strange and bizarre twist, the defence counsel even adopted Doug's inner voice to conjecture upon his thought processes during the Fairview saga.

Anderson wondered how Snider was motivated. He suggested Snider was thinking: "I'm not sick. I'm fine, why am I confined?. . . I got fucked – that fucking College. . . . Should I commit suicide? No. I want a positive self-image. . . . That bastard, Cooper. Why can't he just go away?"

Anderson suggested Dr. Snider wanted nothing else than the lawsuit to be dropped and put forth the argument that in his tortured mind, he may have thought of "rolling over" in the suit and testifying against the other defendants cited.

At one point in Anderson's address to the jury, when he suggested specifically that Doug had doused his own blood around Cooper's office and car so that his "deserted" family could collect on his life insurance after his apparent disappearance, Jean reacted angrily and then broke into tears as the rest of the courtroom fell completely silent. An equally outraged Darren, biting his tongue, put his arm round his weeping mother's shoulder.

Anderson's suggestion bit deep into the core of our family.

Anderson carried on picking at Doug's drinking problem and his fixations with the lawsuit against himself and the other doctors in Fairview. The basis of his case was quite clear. When the two doctors had met in Cooper's office on the night of May 5, 1999, there had, in fact, been no murder, only a false and concocted trail of blood and evidence laid by Snider to incriminate Cooper.

As *The Globe and Mail's* Erin Anderssen wrote, the inference was that, on the very eve of his own retirement, Snider's obsession with Cooper and his hatred for him was greater than Snider's love for his family.

Cooper, said the lawyer, had been an unwitting dupe in the enterprise himself by driving his own car – with Snider's blood on it – to Edmonton Airport to catch his plane to Florida. The defence counsel also claimed that Snider had also smeared blood on Cooper's shirt in his packed duffel bag and on his shoes.

It was an outlandish defence, most observers, agreed. But often, all it takes to demolish a prosecution and thwart a guilty verdict is one juror having a reasonable doubt.

When Anderson had completed his closing argument and the judge and jury had left the courtroom, bridled tensions erupted when Cooper walked up to Jean as she was preparing to leave the courtroom. He said loudly enough for others to hear: "Now, maybe the truth will come out." Already traumatized by what we knew were false and malicious claims by Cooper's defence about Doug's character and motives, we were shocked and angered.

If, in a sense, the defence's closing argument was based on the question of whether Cooper could be so stupid as to leave all sorts of clues behind him in the process of the crime, prosecutor Dave Stilwell, in his closing address, posed the jury with the question of whether anyone, namely Snider, could be so deceitful and cunning as to create the same trail of clues to fake his own disappearance and simultaneously implicate his arch-rival, Cooper.

Stilwell painted a sinister picture of Doug's last hours and minutes on earth. He said Snider, with one phone call, had been lured to Cooper's office on the promise of a peaceful conclusion to the long conflict, had then been overpowered, tortured into writing lies in a false confession, and had ended up pleading for his life.

Stilwell even portrayed the two men physically to enhance what he said was the grim reality of what happened in Cooper's office that night. He pictured Snider as a sedentary homebody fearing he wouldn't be allowed to survive until his 60th birthday in just a few hours' time.

He classified the fitness-conscious Cooper as an intimidating tormentor who, though also 60, was a black belt in Tae Kwan Do bent on exacting fearsome revenge and retribution. Stilwell argued the plot was a clear one – that Cooper had invited Snider to his office to murder him. The prosecutor said that the motive behind the killing was the $3.2 million lawsuit launched by Cooper against, Snider, Chung and Clarke.

And then Stilwell painted more pictures for the minds of the jury members – Snider sitting in Cooper's office slowly writing a handwritten 'confession' copied word for word from a statement typed earlier by Cooper, supposedly admitting to a conspiracy to destroy Cooper's reputation. Stilwell pointedly reflected on the fact that the statement closely mirrored the actual lawsuit that seemed so focal to the case.

The Crown case was that Snider was bullied and coerced into the false confession and then killed by Cooper. There was blood on a paper towel in the garbage can next to the desk where the confession had probably been written. There was blood on a roll of duct tape found on a stool. And there was blood on a carpet near the back door of the office.

"It was all about revenge, money, hatred and contempt", said the prosecutor.

Stilwell drew the jury's attention to the fact that the last sentence of the typed copy of the alleged confession was missing from the handwritten statement. That, said Stilwell, proved that Snider was killed before he could finish, that Cooper was running out of time because he had a plane to catch to Florida.

If Cooper had left such a tell-tale trail of evidence, argued Stilwell, it was likely a result of his contempt for his victim. He had seriously under-estimated the strength of his less active victim during the events in the office and he had had no opportunity to clean up or fix all his mistakes.

According to Stilwell, Cooper was motivated by the belief that he did not have to comply with the expectations of his colleagues or hospital board, that his problems were due to a conspiracy against him, and his desire for revenge and money. Stilwell pointed out that these deeply held beliefs led Cooper to believe that others would agree with him.

Stilwell concurred that Snider did indeed hold resentment for Cooper. But he maintained that in its very tone "it was not violent." He referred to the fact that Snider had admitted to himself in his notes that he had been unable to prevent the arising of resentment, but Stilwell insisted, it was not vindictive, not a motive to disappear.

And, said Stilwell, there was absolutely nothing to indicate sufficiently vindictive disposition towards Cooper as to produce a frame-up. The manner in which his resentments had been so carefully recorded was nowhere close to the actions of a scheming, hostile alcoholic as described by Anderson, the prosecutor maintained.

In one lighter moment, Stilwell referred to the possible sighting of Doug Snider after his disappearance and death. He likened it to an 'Elvis sighting.'

Stilwell coldly dismissed the defence's arguments that Cooper had been framed by Snider. It would have had to be, he said, a plan of "superhuman subtlety and skill."

The case, according to Stilwell, was clear:

That Snider was kept in Cooper's clinic by force or threat of force.

That Snider was dead and Cooper killed him;

That Cooper concealed or destroyed Snider's body;

That Cooper killed Snider on purpose.

The court adjourned.

Part- Six

The Judgement

There is a time for everything,
And a season for every activity under heaven.
A time to be born and a time to die,
A time to plant and a time to uproot,
A time to kill and a time to heal,
A time to tear down and a time to build.
A time to weep and a time to laugh,
A time to mourn and a time to dance,
A time to scatter stones and a time to gather them,
A time to embrace and a time to refrain,
A time to search and a time to give up,
A time to keep and a time to throw away,
A time to tear and a time to mend,
A time to be silent and a time to speak,
A time to love and a time to hate,
A time for war and a time for peace.
— Ecclesiastes 3:1-9 (NIV)[29]

---

[29] Doug read this passage at Lloyd's and my wedding in 1996.

Chapter Twenty-two

On Wednesday morning, October 4, Court of Queen's Bench Justice Joanne Veit began her charge to the jury by reminding jury members that they in reality were the "sole judges of the facts".

They were, said the judge, to "consider carefully, dispassionately without sympathy and prejudice ... facts are the things you choose to believe from the evidence ... stronger than conjecture or speculation."

"Inference," said the judge, "needs proven facts".

Judge Veit reviewed the principles of the law. There must be a presumption of innocence until the Crown proved guilt beyond reasonable doubt. Proof beyond reasonable doubt is the standard that applies to the total body of evidence presented to court. Abe Cooper, she emphasized, was not required to prove anything.

In reference to the huge binder of documents related to Cooper's hospital privileges, the judge suggested the jury were "not to underline the importance of this evidence."

She told the jury: "You must find Dr. Cooper not guilty if after reviewing the evidence, you are not satisfied beyond a reasonable doubt ..."

In the terms of law, she said reasonable doubt was "not imaginary or frivolous doubt", not doubt based on "sympathy or prejudice' but doubt based on "reason and common sense"...doubt logically derived from evidence or absence of evidence. The judge pointed out that while it is almost impossible to prove anything to absolute certainty, "beyond reasonable doubt" is a much higher standard than probability.

Veit elaborated on how the jury should assess the credibility of witnesses noting they need not "fully believe or disbelieve" them. If, for instance, they noted innocent discrepancies, then they should not reject testimony in its entirety.

On the question of what testimony they should accept or how much weight they should attach to testimony, she counseled them to consider whether the witness in question appeared to have memory, whether they were responsive or argumentative, whether they were reasonable and consistent, whether they were consistent with others, whether they appeared impartial.

On evidence, the judge discussed the difference between direct evidence – such as physical evidence found – and circumstantial. Both were admissible as means of proof, she said.

Pointedly, she explained the special rules of this trial regarding character evidence, saying there were different rules in this particular case for Abe Cooper and for Doug Snider.

She said that as regards Cooper, if the jury found that some evidence might reflect badly on his character, they must "not infer directly from that evidence that because of his character, he committed the crime."

She reminded them that they had heard evidence about Dr. Snider's character. "You are entitled to draw on evidence about Dr. Snider's character to decide...for example, did he sign the document willingly?"

In regards to expert witnesses, the judge noted that such witnesses were entitled by law to give opinion evidence on such matters as handwriting analysis, finger printing, DNA analysis, and alcoholism.

On the matter of identification, Veit noted, "observation and memory may be unreliable".

She noted that issues regarding Cooper's hospital privileges were collateral to the trial and could not be used as proof of fact. They had been put into evidence to inform the jury of events that had occurred, to consider the effect of those decisions on Cooper, and to consider whether either party had motive for acting a certain way. Mere motive was insufficient without supporting evidence.

The judge then made reference to excerpts from the Criminal Code. Culpable homicide, murder or manslaughter is to cause death by means of an unlawful act. First-degree murder can be defined as being planned and deliberate. She noted that a person would also be guilty of first-degree murder when a murder was carried out by a person committing forcible confinement.

Veit stated that in order to convict Cooper of first degree murder, the Crown must have proven eight elements, which she listed for the jury. Had the Crown proven beyond a reasonable doubt:

1. That Dr. Snider was dead?
2. That Dr. Cooper caused his death?
3. That Dr. Cooper committed an unlawful act? And if so,
4. That Dr. Cooper's unlawful act caused death?

5. That the time and place was as set out in the indictment?

6. That Dr. Cooper meant to cause death and bodily harm that would cause death?

7. That Dr. Cooper's act was planned and deliberate (and occurred) while confining Dr. Snider?

8. And that Dr. Cooper was the substantial cause of Dr. Snider's death?

Veit then reviewed each point again in more detail. She referred to the fact that no body had been found but said that after considering all the evidence, the jury may still believe Snider was dead.

Had the Crown proven that Dr. Cooper had caused Snider's death by committing an unlawful act?

The Crown, she said, referred to an assault. An assault is the touching of the other person without consent. The jury, she said, did not have to find that such an unlawful act was the sole cause of death but "at least a contributing cause."

Had the Crown proven murder or manslaughter? In the case of murder, the jury had to be satisfied Cooper meant to cause Snider's death or the bodily harm which would cause death. She advised them to use their common sense to draw their inferences. Manslaughter, meanwhile, described a crime when a person killed another person while committing an unlawful act.

The test for first-degree murder was much higher requiring, in addition to the fact that Snider was dead; that Cooper caused his death, that Cooper performed an unlawful act, the murder was planned and deliberate and that Snider was murdered while Cooper was committing the crime of unlawful confinement. She expanded on the meaning of the term 'planned' as "arranged beforehand" and the term 'deliberate' as "carefully thought out, not hasty, not rash."

The judge pointed out that if the jury was satisfied the Crown had proven all the elements she had listed, it would constitute first-degree murder. If the jury thought the Crown had proven the first six elements, it was second-degree murder, and if they thought that the Crown had only proven the first five elements it would be manslaughter.

Veit strongly advised jurors that they should all agree on each point before moving on to the next. She directed the jury to put its questions to her in writing. She encouraged members of the jury to consult with one another to reach a just verdict, as justice "depends on integrity and honesty of ordinary men and women called at random."

She advised jurors to elect a chairperson, urged them to express their point of view in calm and reasonable terms, urged them to listen, not to hesitate to change their mind and reminded them they must be unanimous in their decision.

At noon, the jury left the courtroom to begin its deliberations. For everyone else involved, the long wait had begun. As the jury set about its deliberations, there was nothing more anyone could do except await the verdict.

For our family, this meant long hours seated on black vinyl chairs outside the courtroom along with members of the media and others we had come to know. When leaving the immediate environs of the courtroom, those keeping watch would perhaps go, cell phone in hand, to the courthouse cafeteria or run the gauntlet of ever-present media cameras to slip out to nearby restaurants.

The experience was something akin to a wake, with stories of good times, of reflections on the trial itself and how it appeared to have gone, of speculation on what the jury might be thinking, of hopes and prayers for a satisfactory outcome. Regular contacts were made with those awaiting news from other locations.

The Cooper family and the people in their support network kept a lower profile and likely had found a haven elsewhere in the building, although they were quite often seen in the cafeteria as well.

Meanwhile, the jury continued its work from Wednesday afternoon through Friday evening. Twice during that time, the jury came back for help.

On the first occasion they returned to court to ask for a "complete list of DNA results" from a Crown witness who had explained the DNA results from Snider's blood found in Cooper's Fairview clinic, in Cooper's car and on some of Cooper's clothes. They also asked about photographs taken of garbage that investigators had seized from the clinic.

The next request for help came at about 6 p.m. Friday, October 6. The jury asked permission to bring a question to the judge without the presence of the media. Jurors worried that by asking the question; they would be disclosing the state and progress of their deliberations. Justice Veit advised them that their question would have to be raised in open court.

The jury left, then returned with the request that the judge repeat the instructions regarding item 6 on page 4 of the verdict sheet they had been given – the section regarding "Dr. Cooper meant to cause death and bodily harm that would cause death."

To onlookers, at that moment, it had just become apparent that the jury had at the very least agreed to a verdict of manslaughter and were now deliberating on whether Cooper had committed second degree murder.

Patiently, the judge reviewed the instructions.

The Crown must prove beyond reasonable doubt that Cooper meant to cause the death of Snider, or meant to cause bodily harm which he knew would cause death, and that he, Cooper, was reckless.

The jury returned to its deliberations. Meanwhile, family members, friends and the media stayed close to the courthouse.

At 9:40 p.m., the message reached us that, after 30 hours of deliberation, the jury had finally reached a verdict. People swarmed eagerly back into the courtroom, with members of the two families seating ourselves in clusters in readiness to hear the announcement of the jury's decision.

At 10:05 p.m., the jury foreperson read the verdict ..."not guilty of first-degree murder, guilty of manslaughter."

A collective gasp arose from our family. The decision had been made. Cooper had been found guilty of killing Doug. Although we were relieved that there had been a conviction, we were truly stunned by the manslaughter verdict. The lesser conviction implied that the jury had not unanimously agreed that Cooper had planned to kill Doug; possibly even that Doug's death was an accident.

But it was over. Veit dismissed the jury thanking them for their service. While Cooper was ushered away by the security guard, the courtroom gradually emptied.

Our family, and no doubt Cooper and his family, were considering the implications of this verdict. By the time our contingent gathered to speak to the assembled media outside the courthouse, Cooper's family had sped away in the Nissan car that had been found to contain samples of Doug's blood in May 1999.

Three generations of our family huddled around Darren as he spoke:

When the trial started four weeks ago, our family came looking for answers. We didn't receive anything. Instead we heard our father was alive. What a cruel, what a ridiculous thing to say.

We didn't need a trial to know that our father was dead. The defence strategy was then to paint our father as some kind of monster. If the truth be known, our father was generous, kind, caring and above all else, human.

The verdict came on the Friday evening leading into Thanksgiving weekend.

The next morning, the front page of the *Edmonton Journal* declared:

Cooper guilty of manslaughter.
Victim's family grateful for a guilty verdict, but angry the jury opted for a lesser charge.

And the Edmonton Sun's front page proclaimed:

DOC COOPER GUILTY
But jury finds manslaughter, not murder, in slaying of Dr. Snider.

Chapter Twenty-three

The court reconvened October 11 for the sentencing hearing that afforded our family the opportunity to read victim impact statements. Excerpts of our statements offer a glimpse into the extent of our pain and loss.

Jean read:

I have lost my husband, lover and best friend. In our relationship, he was the spark and I as the kindling....

Doug was proud of his roots. He descended from a God-fearing, loving, warm family. Sadly, the legacy he leaves for our descendants is that of a physician who was murdered. One of Doug's philosophies in life was that 'everyone needs a teddy bear' – I miss my Teddy Bear.

Darren wrote:

I have suffered with the loss attempting to understand what might have happened that night when my father was murdered. I am frustrated knowing that we may never know.... I fear the cruelty will continue long after the trial finishes.

Mavis read on behalf of her and Darren's sons:

Benjamin (nearly seven at the time of his Grandpa's death) in the months to follow, asked why Cooper didn't stop hurting Grandpa when Grandpa said, 'stop' ... and wonders why Abe Cooper does not have to tell the judge the truth about what happened and where Grandpa is.

Cameron was almost five years old when Doug died. He became very fearful that Cooper would kill other members of his family. He believes that Cooper should say he is sorry to Baba and should at least say he is sorry to God.

I am angry that their innocence and sense of security have been ripped away ... Benjamin, Cameron and I love their Grandpa very much and will forever be haunted by not knowing what happened to him and not knowing where he is.

Daena read:

I have to accept that one of the most important people in my life, my Dad, has been brutally and unnecessarily taken from us. . . . . I cannot understand why the accused does not have to answer for his actions wholly and truthfully. I believe justice is about the truth. . . . I want the accused to realize what his actions have done to me and my family.

Douglas Dean read:

> This fear of how my father died is perpetuated by a sadness that my father has not had a proper funeral; instead his body was left to rot alone and lost in a vast, cold wilderness … It is not fair for a man who spent so much of his life healing others to be taken in such circumstances. My father deserved more than that. Any human being does.

On behalf of our father, who was seated in the courtroom, I read:

> Doug was my only son…He was always concerned about me and the rest of the family. This is the hardest thing that has happened to me. It's difficult in the first place to lose a son but under these conditions, it's harder. It's hard to believe that someone could do that…

Mary read:

> When I was able to sleep, I would wake hoping that it was a bad dream. Now I know that my brother is dead. I cry when I think of what torture and pain he must have suffered…. He had no family to comfort him those last moments before his death. We were unable to say 'goodbye.' With Doug's death, I have no closure and the hurt returns again and again.

When finished reading her statement, Mary turned to Abe and added:

> Abe Cooper was a doctor and surgeon. When my brother was bleeding, why didn't he stop the bleeding?

My own statement concluded with an appeal to the judge:

> I wonder what I can do to ensure that what has happened to my brother doesn't happen to someone else … He has been silenced. Will it be safe for others to speak the truth or will we too be silenced? That is my fear.

Our cousin, Dave, read a poignant statement describing his persistent, haunted thoughts regarding his cousin's death and the whereabouts of his body. Sharon, Doug's sister-in-law, read a statement on behalf of her father, Art Pahal, who was deeply affected by the loss of his son-in-law.

Following a recess, the court reconvened to hear arguments by the Crown and the defence regarding an appropriate sentence for Cooper.

Crown prosecutor Stilwell told the attentive audience that not for a moment had the accused, Cooper, accepted that he could ever be in the wrong. He was apparently incapable of accepting the simple fact that his problems were caused by his own conduct.

On one matter of evidence, the prosecutor insisted again that it was absolutely clear that the accused himself had typed the documents that purported to be Snider's "confession" of misdemeanors and transgressions.

The Crown lawyer spoke of the continuing injury to the bereaved because the victim's body has not been found. He said:

> Others must be deterred from similar uncivil conduct. Others must be deterred from adding further cruel and wrongful action to killing.

Stilwell also commented that the accused was incapable of being deterred. He feared Cooper, though not an old man, would never accept his responsibility for events, that he had not and would never respect the law, that he could never be rehabilitated. Stilwell stressed that we must be seen as being a "just, peaceful and safe society." He added that those whom Cooper claimed were "conspirators" had:

> a right to believe that they could be targets of violence ... and a right to be assured that they would not be harmed.

For all these reasons, the prosecutor argued that life imprisonment would be a reasonable sentence for Cooper.

Defence counsel Anderson, on the other hand, suggested that a sentence in the four-to-six year range would be appropriate in the case. Clinically, in a statement that I saw as mockery of our impact statements, Anderson cautioned the judge to be "careful not to let emotional expressions distort case".

Anderson also stated that Cooper's assertion of innocence ought not be an aggravating factor. Anderson referred to a contentious case of a man charged with the murder of his wife although no body had been found. The case had resulted in an ongoing process of convictions followed by successful appeals. In that case, the man in question had been found to be psychopathic.

"That is not the situation here," Anderson maintained.

I cynically wondered how the defence lawyer knew this, as Cooper had never been officially assessed. The defence argued that character evidence, as it was, did not support the position of the Crown.

When Judge Veit invited Dr. Cooper to make a statement, he rose and said:

> Doug Snider has been seen twice (since May 5)... my private detective has seen him... I am completely confident that within the year I

will know the whereabouts of Dr. Snider and when I do, I will share it with the Press.

On this, the *Edmonton Journal's* David Staples was to write:

> As Cooper finished speaking, it was great to hear Snider's family fill the courtroom with laughter, for a moment. Cooper's spell had been broken. The Boogie man was revealed as a bent, twisted and seemingly deluded crackpot. Doesn't get any sweeter than that.[30]

Later, in answer to media questions on Cooper's statement, I simply said it was hardly worthy of a comment.

The court adjourned while the judge considered her ruling on the sentence. When court reconvened later that afternoon, the judge reviewed her assessment of the evidence supporting the conviction. One statement stood out for me:

> Cooper did not accept the decisions of others ... (but it) would not be fair to characterize him as aggressive or assaultive.

I noted that evidence to the contrary had not been allowed. The judge spoke of evidence establishing Cooper actively sought "to have others accept his view."

However, Veit did note that her ruling took into account aggravating factors including the fact that the crime occurred in the context of civil litigation and the failure of Cooper to reveal the location of Doug's body. The sentence imposed was ten years minus time already served – reducing it to seven years and four months. (Cooper will complete his sentence in February 2008.) In accordance with the law, Cooper was also banned, from the date of his release, against having a firearm for one year.

Again, our family met the media outside the courthouse. Darren made a brief statement expressing our family's disappointment in the sentence.

In an interview with CBC television later that day, I stated that our family was more concerned about fairness, public safety and accountability by the offender than retribution or revenge. I pointed out the Court's failure to pay attention to the offender's pattern of blaming others for his difficulties and his apparent inability to take responsibility for his actions.

---

[30] "Queries that cut to the heart", *Edmonton Journal*, October 12, 2000, A3.

Chapter Twenty-four

Maintaining his innocence, Cooper appealed the verdict. The appeal was heard and dismissed by the Alberta Court of Appeal in October 2002.

The Crown appealed Cooper's sentence arguing that Justice Veit had not imposed a just and appropriate sentence "reflecting the gravity of the offense committed and the moral blameworthiness of the offender," and that the sentence did not adequately reflect "the principles of deterrence, retribution and denunciation".

The appeal was heard in December 2002 and dismissed on July 23, 2003. The Court's memorandum of judgment stated that without evidence of how Snider met his death,

> the sentencing judge neither assumed the least culpable circumstance, or the most. She recognized the gravity of the offence and the high degree of responsibility of the offender. She could not go further without the danger of finding facts contrary to the verdict....

It concludes:

> The question is not what sentence we would have imposed, but whether the sentence imposed is demonstrably unfit. We are not persuaded that it is.[31]

In August 2003, the Supreme Court of Canada dismissed Cooper's request for a hearing.

On December 11, 2003, more than three years after the sentencing hearing, Judge Veit ordered that a sample of Cooper's DNA be submitted to the National DNA Bank within 90 days before he leaves prison.

Veit delayed this hearing until after Cooper's appeals were exhausted. The Crown appealed the judge's right to delay this matter arguing that the federal DNA legislation had taken away the judge's discretionary powers. However, the Crown's appeal was dismissed in May 2002 by an Appeal Court panel that ruled the language in the legislation is ambiguous and "does not meet exacting standards."

One year after Cooper's claim that he would find Doug, a follow-up story by Lisa Gregoire for the *Edmonton Journal* noted that

---

[31] Memorandum of Judgment in the Court of Appeal of Alberta filed July 23, 2003.

Our father, George Schattschneider stands by the tree planted in Doug's memory. Photo: Edmonton Journal.

Cooper hadn't been able to act on his "idle boast" that he would prove that Doug was still alive.

She reported that, on the second anniversary of Doug's death, our family planted an oak tree in memory of our loved one in the cemetery of the family church. I was quoted as saying, "We have been deprived of a normal course of grieving.... We're taking back the dignity of victims to show respect for their loved ones."[32]

On May 5, 2001, two years after Doug's death, The *Edmonton Sun* reported that Jean Snider had launched a $1 million lawsuit against Cooper:

In the statement of claim, Jean Snider alleges when Cooper invited her husband into his office, Cooper had a duty to ensure Dr. Snider was safe while he was in the building. She claims Cooper was responsible for the safety of those using the office. It's alleged Cooper breached this duty by doing things that hurt and eventually killed Dr. Snider, Cooper created a 'hazardous situation' and failed to 'assist Dr. Snider once it became reasonably foreseeable that the injuries suffered would cause death.'[33]

The following day, a story in the *Edmonton Journal* quoted Darren:

It's two years to the date since our father's life was taken. And after much deliberation, our family felt it was necessary to commence a civil suit.

The lawsuit is not motivated by money or vindictiveness, but rather is intended to help provide us with answers as a means of defending ourselves.

Our primary objective is to find our father's remains so we can have a burial. And secondly, despite the criminal conviction, our father's

---

[32] "The Search for Dr. Snider" *Edmonton Journal*, October 11, 2001, A1.
[33] "Victim's wife sues killer Doc", *Edmonton Sun*, May 5, 2001, p.3.

killer continues to be active with a lawsuit against our family. I don't think we have a choice.[34]

On January 30, 2002, Kevin Feth, lawyer who acted on behalf of the sued doctors and Mistahia Health region, requested that Cooper's civil lawsuit be dismissed in accordance with the "drop dead rule' that applies when no action is taken in a civil suit for five years or when there is inordinate delay or prejudice. Feth stated that the dismissal lifts a cloud that has been hanging over the Health authority and doctors for nearly five years. Judge Walter Breitkreuz awarded the doctors and health authorities more than $20,000 in costs to be paid by Cooper.

After serving two thirds of his sentence, Cooper, would have been due for statutory release from prison on September 1, 2005. However, in December 2004, Corrections Canada referred Cooper to the National Parole Board for a detention hearing. The National Parole Board can order that an offender be detained in prison beyond his statutory release date when it is satisfied that if the offender is released in the community, he is likely to commit an offence causing death or serious harm.

The hearing was held on May 20, 2005 at Bowden Institution where Cooper is incarcerated. The parole officer presented the reason for the hearing. Cooper, who was found guilty of committing a violent offence, continues to deny his guilt, claims that he is a victim of conspiracy, maintains that Snider is still alive and has refused to participate in rehabilitation. He is consumed with a plan to find Snider and get back at people who placed him in this position. His threats to use legal tools are similar to what consumed him prior to the killing.

An intake assessment on Cooper's admission to the institution, revealed that he presented with symptoms of disordered personality including underlying hostility, fear of social disapproval, high self-regard and sense of entitlement. It concluded that he possibly had a narcissistic personality disorder characterized by insecurity and competitiveness to prove self-worth. The report states further that Cooper deals with the stress of his conviction by fantasizing people's reaction when his conviction is overturned.

A number of our family attended the hearing. Members of the media, Corrections Canada and National Parole Board staff were present. Detective Will Tonowski of the Behavioral Assessment

---

[34] "Snider family says its $1M suit aimed at finding MD's body", *Edmonton Journal*, May 6, 2001, A6.

Unit, High Risk Offender Section of the Edmonton City Police, was also in attendance.

Our family members each stood to read our victim impact statements that asked haunting questions about Cooper's actions on the night of the crime and concern about further retaliatory actions.

Daena's written statement on behalf of her family was on file:

> The trauma you inflicted on our father and family has shattered us. I always believed in God's power and had great faith, as that is what my father taught us to believe...

> You took my father's life but you could NEVER take away the man he was, the values he instilled in us or the positive influence he left on the many lives he touched. In taking his life you re-enforced our love for him and our family has been drawn even closer. He is an ever present grandfather with the stories we tell and a loving father with the memories we hold close. He is still remembered as a loyal devoted husband and a much loved dedicated physician. But all of that still cannot fill the void of his physical absence.

> Several of my family members opted not to appear at the hearing or provide a written statement because they feel threatened by your release...There is an overwhelming fear that you are not finished what you started and that your 'pattern' of abuse and threats will continue.

Dave, our cousin, read:

> I have been working with the Restorative Opportunities Program to set up a meeting with us in a controlled setting. This would give you an opportunity to accept responsibility and tell us your side of the story, which would include what you did with Doug's body. I challenge you to accept this responsibility and do the right thing. All you have to do is contact your parole officer when you are ready....

> The prisoner in responding to my request for a meeting with him said 'When I'm released from prison, I intend to find Dr. Snider and put him in jail.' The fear that raises is maybe the prisoner has convinced himself that Doug's still alive and if on his release he's going to go looking for him, the obvious place for him to start would be Doug's family. Who knows what might happen then.

Mary read:

> As we look at family pictures, it is hard to explain to my grandchildren that Uncle Doug died and went to heaven. They ask, 'How did

he die? Was he old and sick?' No. The oldest says, 'A bad man killed him. Why Grandma?' To this question, I have no answer.

I saw my brother as a happy man who trusted Abraham Cooper when he went to meet with him the evening of May 5, 1999. Doug hoped to settle the grievances Abraham Cooper had against him but instead walked into a trap...I believe Abraham Cooper intended my brother, Doug Snider to die and I fear he could offend again.

My statement, written directly to Abe Cooper, concluded:

How can I be sure that you will not harm those you hate or perceive as a threat?

We need the assurance that you will not and cannot re-enter our lives. I do not seek revenge but continue to ask for your accountability so that we (including you and your family) can all move on in peace.

Cooper, dressed in a green shirt and blue jeans, sat slouched in this chair with his back to us, seated a couple of rows behind him. In front of him, he had copies of our statements with sections highlighted. Apparently he was more interested in challenging the statements than truly hearing the messages that they conveyed.

When Colleen R. Ryan, Parole Board panel member, invited Cooper's response, he declared that he would not be intimidated by lies and hysteria... He claimed that he was going to find Snider and put him in prison and "all these victims can take their statements and put them in the garbage dump." (Later, Cooper's "assistant" did suggest that the victim impact statements contained matters of conjecture not proven in court. However, he did not delve into the statements as Cooper had requested.)

When questioned by the three-person panel, Cooper, declaring that he was now bankrupt, defiantly repeated his threat to sue those who were responsible for putting him in prison and reiterated his past grievances with the Fairview physicians and Health Board.

Ryan pointed out to Cooper that litigation is part of his offence cycle. "The evidence shows that when you're involved in a civil litigation, the outcome is manslaughter."

The panel deliberated for one hour after the two hour hearing and returned with its decision. John A. Lindsay, speaking for the panel, emphasized that the test for detention is risk. The panel drew heavily on the psychological risk assessment from April 2001, the only assessment in which Cooper participated. It noted that Cooper had been referred but refused to attend the aggressive behavior control program. He also had limited interest in exploring issues around the offense.

Lindsay stated:

> You are consumed with the emotion of your fight ... yet, you don't present as an emotional man. You have refused all core programming and made no progress in risk reduction.

He noted that while the last psychological assessment was more favorable, Cooper had not participated in it and it looked at many factors in his life before he engaged in crime. Lindsay expressed the panel's concern that:

> You have not taken the opportunity to explain yourself...
> The Board is disappointed in your contempt for the positions of the victims.

The panel made it clear that it accepted the conclusion of the Court; that is, the conviction of manslaughter, and noted substantial evidence of Cooper's indifference to the crime, lack of remorse or compassion for his victims.

The Parole Board's written report stated:

> At the hearing you were asked to explain what you meant by the plan when you are released to 'go after everyone that lied to put me in here.' You generally replied that you would require them to 'show up in a court of law and be cross-examined, and then we'll know who the liars are.' You continued by saying that you wanted criminal charges to be laid against these parties for perjury, and you specifically identified the prosecutor who you believe 'deliberately lied'. You did qualify these statements by adding that 'you've never threatened anyone,' although the Board noted that in returning to this subject on different occasions you also said other things: in respect to your conviction – 'I understand. It's not the end of it ...'; in respect of your potential for conflict, '... if someone pushes me around, look out ...' and concerning your victim, Dr. Snider, 'he should have killed me when he had the chance.' You claimed to be a 'fighter' – which the Board understands in the context of 'determined' – who would settle for nothing less than (in your words) 'a withdrawal of all the charges, a public apology, formal compensation, and an inquiry into all the people who lied.'

In reference of Cooper's pattern of violent behavior, the report noted:

A) (ii) ...You were originally charged with the offence of murder, but were convicted of manslaughter. In any event, the life of another human being was taken as a result of your criminal offending. Forensic evidence strongly suggests, but cannot prove, that your offence involved a physical altercation and quite likely the use of a weapon which has been 'surmised' to be a scalpel or other similar blade.' The offense was negatively commented upon by the presiding Justice as having arisen out of civil litigation where there is an expectation that emotions will be controlled and restrained- which by your conviction you are unable to do. . .

(vi) ... This crime is brutal in and of itself owing to the death of the victim. The Board also notes that the injury to the bereaved members of the victim's family continues to this day owing to the fact that you have not disclosed how, or where, you disposed of the body. . .

(vii) ... You have repeatedly denied the offence despite having been properly convicted; you have also never expressed any remorse or compassion for the victim or his family. The Board considers such sustained conduct to be characteristic of "substantial indifference. . .

The Board remains concerned by the file reference from intake which shows your unwillingness to discuss your offending, but your willingness to accept and partially agree without comment or reply with the statement that 'it must take a certain amount of anger or simple ruthlessness with traits of psychopathy to kill another person and dispose of the body.' At the hearing your response to what you accepted or agreed with was not very helpful.

The report concludes:

The Board has determined that your plans, as soon as you leave the institution, are to engage in seeking the redress which you believe you are owed. The Board also believes that you will likely do anything to secure the end you think to be just – in accordance with your judgment of that term. You have already done this, and a victim died. You are re-entering the crime cycle that previously caused this harm if indeed you have ever left it. Without your help, assistance or cooperation the Board – and the Correctional Service of Canada – is unable to be more precise.

In the opinion of the Board there is no supervision program in the community with adequate structure or support to effectively manage the risk which you present.

As a result of reviewing your file and hearing your presentation today the Board has concluded that, if released, you are likely to commit an offense causing serious harm to another person before the expiration of the sentence you are now serving according the law. Accordingly, the Board orders your detention."[35]

When advised that the detention order would be reviewed in one year's time, Cooper replied bluntly, "I won't appear before this panel again."

Following the hearing, Jean, Mary and I met the media outside the prison gate. I made a brief statement on behalf of our family:

> We are relieved with the decision of the Parole Board and are grateful for at least one more year of safety. We have learned that Abe hasn't changed. We appreciate the careful review and deliberations by the Parole Board regarding this situation.

Cooper's subsequent appeal of the Parole Board's ruling was dismissed in July 2005.

Jean, Hazel and Mary walking to meet the media in front of Bowden Institution after detention hearing, May 2005.

Photo: Edmonton Journal.

---

[35] National Parole Board Detention Review Decision Sheet, Abraham Robert Cooper, 2005/05/20

Chapter Twenty-five

So how is it possible that an innocent victim of murder could be put on trial himself? For our family, it was unbelievable – at least until we personally came face to face with the Canadian criminal justice system for the first time.

In many ways, it should be said; the 'system' did work. Police followed and gathered the trail of evidence with great care and attention. An arrest was made and a charge of first-degree murder was laid. After a series of court appearances and a preliminary inquiry, sixteen months later, Abe Cooper's trial began.

But then the focus shifted from Abe to Doug, the victim. Since Doug's body had not been found, the defence set out to prove that Doug was not dead. The testimony of two truck drivers that maybe, just maybe, they had seen Doug, gave the defence lawyer the license he needed to take a position that Doug, the victim, was the guilty party. The real reason for the trial, that is, whether the defendant was guilty or not, seemed to become secondary to the defence's assault on my brother.

In the end, the jury did not buy the argument that Doug was alive, but evidently one or more jury members weren't convinced that Cooper could have planned the whole thing, otherwise Cooper wouldn't have escaped with a conviction on the lesser charge of manslaughter.

Apparently, the judge didn't believe he could have been as malicious and aggressive as the records showed, because in sentencing Cooper, she minimized the risk that he posed. It is worth bearing in mind that the Crown argued that such evidence was available and tried to have it introduced into the trial. The judge had ruled it inadmissible.

The Cooper trial was somehow reminiscent of trials such as, for instance, that of OJ Simpson, in which the defence put police and victims on trial while OJ remained silent. I wondered skeptically if the Cooper defence strategy was following that example, claiming a set up and the planting of evidence. After all, it had worked for OJ, hadn't it?

It did work for Cooper too, at least in part. He was able to use his trial to assassinate Doug's character and malign him all over again, this time with an even larger audience. He has been convicted, but thus far still refuses to take responsibility, or to inform the police of the whereabouts of Doug's body. He continues to claim a conspiracy that now, according to him, includes justice officials and witnesses at his trial.

The double standard of the criminal justice system became readily apparent from the first day of the Cooper trial. The first rule is that a defendant is innocent until proven guilty beyond a reasonable doubt, and the second, although not stated up front, is that the due process rights of the defendant override any rights of the victim. Abuse of this privilege can be devastating for the victims of crime, or in this case, for their bereaved families.

The imbalance between the rights of defendants and victims can be attributed to the Canadian Charter of Rights and Freedoms, which since it became law in 1982, has upheld the rights of the accused as paramount. Rather than encourage persons who are guilty to be truthful and take responsibility for their crimes, the law allows them to remain silent.

Alex Macdonald, a former Attorney General for the province of British Columbia, begins his book, *Outrage* with this bold statement:

> Canada's legal system is heading for disaster, so preoccupied with protecting individual's rights that it fails to protect the rights of society. More than fair to a few, the legal system is less than fair to the majority of Canadians, sacrificing time-honored concepts such as Truth and Justice to an unhealthy fascination with process. [36]

When the Charter protects the rights of special individuals, such as those accused of a crime, the rights and interests of the average citizen or society at large may be violated. Much is said about equality rights, yet it seems that victims or potential victims of crime, who are not named in the Charter, do not have rights equal to those of the accused. Many do not recognize or wish to acknowledge that paradox.

Would inclusion of victims' rights in the Charter make a difference? Not likely, according to Alan Young, professor at Osgoode Hall Law School and author of *Justice Defiled*.[37] In a panel discussion at the National Victims' Conference in November 2003, Young stated that constitutional changes could make a difference for victims of crime only after there are changes in the legal culture.

---

[36] Macdonald, Alex, *Outrage: Canada's Justice System on Trial*, Raincoast, Vancouver, 1999, preface v.

[37] Young, Alan N., *Justice Defiled*, Key Porter, Toronto, 2003.

Victims' rights were addressed in the 1985 United Nations Declaration of the Basic Principles of Justice for Victims of Crimes and Abuse of Power. This document became the basis for a Canadian document, "The Canadian Statement of Basic Principles of Justice for Victims of Crime", originally written in 1988 and revised in 2003.

The principles emphasize courtesy, compassion, respect, information sharing and protection of the victim from intimidation and retaliation. The statement is not law so cannot be enforced. Principle 8 states:

> The views, concerns and representations of victims are an important consideration in criminal justice processes and should be considered in accordance with prevailing law, policies and procedures. [38]

This principle describes the double standard and gives the answer to any possible dilemma; that is, while victims' views should be considered, the prevailing law still rules. Our family learned that our concerns about the unfair and false attack on their loved one had no weight in court. The process ran according to the rule of law with no provision for protecting the victim's dignity.

In the Cooper trial, evidence that supported his motive for committing the crime was ruled inadmissible by the judge who deemed that it was more prejudicial than probative. As a result, the jury did not have all the facts. Meanwhile, the law gave the defence lawyer great latitude in his assassination of the victim.

As long as the judge determined that the defence had some "air of reality", he was allowed to proceed. Experts agree that it is a "fine line" to draw on such a matter.

The lawyers and the judge in the Cooper trial wrangled over the admissibility of evidence for hours. The scene might be likened to that of a game in which the defence had the advantage by being allowed to chalk up points against the victim while the Crown was not allowed to score points against the accused. The rules seemed to be more about winning than knowing the truth.

In a jury trial, jury members are expected to determine if the Crown has proven beyond a reasonable doubt the guilt of the defendant. That decision is based only on evidence ruled admissible by the judge. With limited information and little, if any, preparation in group process, the jury is expected to come to consensus.

---

[38] *http://Canada.justice.gc.ca/en/ps/voc/csbp.html*

If unable to agree, either some compromise is made or the jury is "hung" and the case has to be retried.

Jury members are selected from a pool of members of the public who are considered peers of the defendant. But what does it really mean to be tried by one's peers? Is it truly a random collection of unbiased persons representing a cross-section of age, education, life and work experience, race and gender or is it really a selection of persons who are available to serve on a jury and who are deemed acceptable by the lawyers?

Publication bans are imposed on pretrial evidence in order to ensure that the public or pool of potential jurors is not tainted by information that may contribute to bias or preconceived notions of guilt or innocence.

We were conscientious about honoring the publication ban placed on pre-trial evidence in the Cooper trial, and for example, did not place a Memoriam notice in the newspaper on the first and second anniversary of Doug's death. We were cautioned not to as it could have unduly influenced the jury pool.

The publication ban imposed on evidence disclosed at the Gomery Inquiry into the sponsorship scandals in Quebec in 2005 was lifted following an outcry that the public had a right to know how public money had been squandered.

In pre-trial hearings regarding charges against Robert Pickton in the alleged murders of women from Vancouver Eastside, the defence lawyer attempted to limit information from leaking out to the public. However, the B.C. Supreme Court Justice James Williams denied the application. *The Province* newspaper reported:

> He said a section of the Criminal Code that spells out the scope of publication bans in pre-trial hearings is sufficient in the Pickton case. In a novel twist, he added the Internet to the Criminal Code ban on publication of pre- jury proceedings.[39]

When the lack of knowledge about the case becomes the criteria for jury selection, informed, knowledgeable jurors who are well qualified are likely eliminated. Macdonald argues:

> Surely an informed juror, one who may have followed news reports about an inquiry, can decide impartially on the evidence…The uninformed, uninterested juror is far worse, bringing to court ill-founded biases and gossip.[40]

---

[39] "Judge throws out gag order requested by Pickton lawyer", *The Province*, June 9, 2005, A10.

[40] Macdonald, A, p. 161.

Amendments to the Criminal Code in 1999 gave victims new rights in the criminal justice process. Victims may read a statement that describes the effects of the crime on their lives. Victims are told that their statements will not affect the verdict but may influence the sentence and the offender's eligibility for parole. They are to speak only about their own experience, say nothing negative about the offender and until recently, the statements were released to the defence before the trial.[41]

Authorities claim that Victim Impact Statements are a breakthrough for victims' rights. But legal professionals, whose arguments and rulings are based on reason, distance themselves from victims' pain. Is the court ready and able to hear emotional expressions without being inclined to discount or dismiss them?

Since our family prepared our victim impact statements well in advance of the trial, the statements did not reflect the revictimizing effects of the trial itself. Only after the trial did we speak publicly about the inaccuracy and cruelty of the defence position. Shaken and feeling betrayed by the whole experience, still intimidated and afraid of jeopardizing future proceedings, we were guarded in our criticism of the justice system at that time.

Malcolm Maye's political cartoon. Edmonton Journal, October 12, 2000.

---

[41] The practice of disclosing victim impact statements in advance to the defence was recently challenged in the Alberta Court of Queen's Bench. A ruling by the Honorable Justice Brian Burrows in January 2004 now states that impact statements need not be disclosed until after a conviction.

We were shocked and disappointed with the system we had expected would seek truth and justice. Others shared in that disillusionment, as illustrated in the cartoon in the *Edmonton Journal* the day after Cooper's sentencing. The Lady of Justice was depicted with her arms bound.

So where do crime victims find justice? Will the scales of justice balance themselves? Not likely without the voices of victims of crime and their advocates.[42]

Kent Roach, University of Toronto law professor, writes in his review of the evolution of criminal law in Canada:

> The victims of crime cannot be ignored. In the worlds of prosecution and punishment, they can be informed and consulted, but will have little real decision-making power. Some victims' rights will be recognized, but they will often be pitted against due-process rights. In the worlds of crime prevention and restorative justice, however, victims and potential victims of crime may find more decision-making power and less opposition.One hopes that they-all of us ultimately-can find more security and satisfaction.[43]

But some victims of crime remain skeptical of the benefit of restorative justice initiatives for victims. To date, restorative justice tends to cater more to the offender than the victim.[44] Perpetrators of crime are given the opportunity to make amends for their crime when they hear about its impact on their victims. But not all offenders can or will take responsibility for their actions.

A restorative approach can only be effective when the offender is capable of empathy, true remorse and willing to learn from the intervention. Given the nature of Cooper's crime and his attitude and behavior since the crime, restorative justice would not be an option. Doug lost his life taking a conciliatory approach.

In the hope that Cooper might have had a change of heart, Dave Drager, our cousin, did seek assistance through the Restorative Opportunities Program to arrange a meeting with Cooper to discuss, in particular, the whereabouts of Doug's body. Cooper rejected that invitation.

Of course, reparation and healing for all concerned is more probable and possible when the offender is able to accept responsibility for his crime. A natural response for persons violated and betrayed by a system supposedly designed to protect them is to call

---

[42] See Appendix II, p. 177, for my summary of what I have learned about the criminal justice system. Note that this was written in 2004 and pertains to the first five years of my experience with the justice system.

[43] Roach, Kent, *Due Process and Victims' Rights*, University of Toronto, 1999, p. 319.

[44] Report of Alberta Victims of Crime Consultation, 2002, p.18.

for accountability and change. It is part of the healing process. Driven by my indignation and desire for answers, I have written letters to persons in authority in the justice system.

I began soon after the trial with a passionate letter to Ministers of Justice for the province of Alberta and the government of Canada. I knew from the beginning that I needed to address both jurisdictions. The federal government enacts criminal law while provincial governments are responsible for the administration of justice. That letter was a first step towards calling for accountability by both Cooper and the justice system.[45]

Responses by judicial and legal authorities to my inquiries and appeals for justice reform over the past six years defend the delicate balancing of the rights of all those involved in the process. Some politely express regret for the victim's loss and provide assurance and information about initiatives on behalf of victims. But few offer promises for reform in the law that contributes to the revictimization of victims-the persons who live with the aftermath of crime.

The 2002 report of a consultation with surviving family members in cases where there has been a death due to homicide, vehicle or air crash, in order to determine problems, impacts and issues arising from services, policies or legislation, is aptly named "No End to the Pain". The following quotes from the report say it well.

> Many families emphasized that the duration of grief, often reinforced by contacts with the criminal justice system, was particularly difficult to bear. Families frequently note that "the pain never ends" and that their only recourse was to learn to live with it on a daily basis.

> Families are shocked, exhausted and depleted after experiencing the violent death of a loved one. For most families, the death is not the end but the beginning of a long, exhausting and painful struggle-often at every stage of the process and often lasting their entire lives. Families are shocked to find that in the period of their lowest energy they must fight for considerations they think should have been theirs by right.[46]

I have moved beyond the events of May 1999 to see the bigger picture of a society where violence is all too prevalent. Yet victims of violence are all too often silenced and ignored.I describe the experiences of victims or survivors of violence in an article entitled, "After Violence Strikes" published in *MACLEAN'S* magazine in September 2003.[47]

In January 2004, I appealed to the Federal Minister of Justice:

---

[45] See Appendix III, page 178.
[46] 'No End to the Pain", Focus Consultants, Victoria, British Columbia, 2002, p.vii, 34.
[47] "After Violence Strikes", *MACLEAN'S*, September 1, 2003, p. 46.

Changes are needed in the law, the constitution and the attitudes of the legal profession in order to ensure that victims cannot be put on trial while defendants' rights are protected. Perpetrators of crime ought to account for their actions instead of being allowed to further victimize the victim. Surely this is a matter of human rights for victims.

Honorable Irwin Cotler replied:

Please be assured that issues relating to the needs of victims of crime are treated with the highest priority by the Department Of Justice Canada. I am aware that Canadians are increasingly concerned about the treatment of victims in the justice system, and I assure you that the interests of victims are of the utmost importance throughout the criminal process.[48]

A year later, our family was about to experience the workings of another part of the criminal justice system governed by the Corrections and Conditional Release Act under the jurisdiction of the Minister of Public Safety and Solicitor General.

Members of our family met the legal criteria to qualify as "victims of crime". A victim is defined as "someone to whom harm was done or who suffered physical or emotional damage as the result of an offense". When the victim has died, a spouse, partner or relative may request and receive information about the offender that is usually protected under the Privacy Act. This includes notification of any escape or future failure to report while on release, and information regarding decisions of Parole Board hearings. Information regarding the offender's progress while incarcerated is made available to victims only when a hearing is held.[49]

In December 2004, we were informed that Corrections Canada had referred Abe Cooper for a detention hearing. We learned that this unusual step was being taken because Corrections Canada was apparently concerned that Cooper might offend again if he was released on his statutory release date (two years and five months) before the completion his sentence.

It was reassuring, on one hand, that the system was addressing a safety concern but frightening to realize that, even if the offender was detained, he would still be released in February 2008. Wondering again why the matter of public safety is not routinely addressed in the sentencing process, I addressed my questions to

---

[48] Correspondence from Honorable Irwin Cotler, Minister of Justice and Attorney General of Canada, July 6, 2004.

[49] An Information Guide to Assist Victims: Federal Corrections and Conditional Release, Solicitor General Canada.

the federal Minister of Public Safety and Solicitor General. I did not receive an answer.

Ironically, the letter was sent only days before the tragic shooting of four RCMP officers in Mayerthorpe, Alberta. The matter of public safety was placed front and center in the media, the minds of the public and politicians and the hearts of the victims' families. James Roszko, the killer, had a history of sexual defiant behavior, had been convicted for sexual assault and "was known for his temper, love of guns and hatred of police."[50]

The incident highlighted the system's apparent inability to address the problems posed by troubled individuals who bully and intimidate others, nurture their grievances and are capable of horrendous acts of violence. It also raised questions regarding the root causes of such hatred and contempt. Some could see obvious parallels between the conduct of Roszko and Cooper.

At Cooper's detention hearing with the National Parole Board, members of the panel hearing did recognize the threat that he posed to public safety and the likelihood he would re-offend.

I observed that while those representing the National Parole Board and Corrections Canada honored Cooper's rights, they also took our concerns seriously. Was that because since the conviction, according to the law, we had certain rights? Or was it simply because the persons involved were more concerned about risk management and victims' needs?

Finally, it seemed, the long history of this man's bullying and disruptive behavior, and the danger he posed for those he perceived as a threat, was recognized. But his determination and threats to get even was now sweeping an even wider swath to include more innocent and potential victims.

Victim safety had been given priority in the investigation stage of this case and, once charges were laid, was addressed again in the bail hearing. But why did the judge not address his matter more fully during the trial and sentencing process? Protection of the privacy and integrity of the deceased victim and his family did not appear to be a concern. Rather, the defendant, through his lawyer, was allowed to continue his attacks against the man who, the jury later decided, had been his victim.

Referring to Cooper's concealment of Doug's body after his crime, the Crown lawyer argued that others should be deterred from similar conduct. He warned that the offender was incapable

---

[50] "30 Years of violence, sexual aggression", *Edmonton Journal*, March 5, 2005, A5.

of being deterred and appealed for protection of those who could be at risk of being harmed in the future. Even then, the sentence did not take into account the depth and breadth of cooper's vindictiveness, the complexity of his character and conduct, and any likelihood of his ongoing threat to public safety.

Ironically, after weeks of deliberation in the trial, the sentencing process seemed to progress very quickly. Did it not deserve the same care and attention as was given to ensuring due process for the defendant in the earlier stages of the proceedings?

This case encapsulated the concerns of so many people in Canada and in other democratic societies. Legal professionals can become so preoccupied with the interpretation of the law and protection of the defendant's rights that they can become desensitized to other realities before them. Trained to make the system work, lawyers may be blinded to the human side of violent crime and its impact on victims, families and communities. Authorities may ignore the real possibility that defendants/offenders with a disproportional sense of entitlement will abuse their rights and privileges.

In a speech at an international conference on corrections and prisons, District Court Judge E.C.P. Pratt from Queensland, Australia, summarized the sentencing problem this way:

> The purposes of sentencing still bring into focus, despite their flaws, the traditional theories of retribution, deterrence and rehabilitation. The basic philosophy of most countries including Australia and Canada is now rehashed as three principles: 'just desserts',[51] proportionality and equality, a philosophy which still pays little attention to the possibility that a prisoner may be suffering from a severe personality disorder that renders him incorrigible. . . .
>
> We still refuse to acknowledge that there exist in each of our communities a hard core of people who can't or won't stop offending.[52]

The Canadian psyche has difficulty believing that some people are actually capable of deliberately harming others without any sense of responsibility or remorse. Offenders are expected to cooperate and respond to rehabilitation programs. Only when the offender is ready for release, it seems, does the system seriously concern itself with assessing risk to the safety of the public.

Greater social and political awareness and legislative reform is necessary in order that perpetrators are held accountable for their

---

[51] A notion of retributive justice that persons deserve to be treated the same way they treat others.

[52] Pratt, E.C.P., "The Current Criminal Justice System: How do we measure up?" Inaugural conference of International Association of Corrections and Prisons, Budapest, Hungary, October 1999. *www.courts.qld.gov.au*

crimes and that the rights of victims of crime are protected. Better education of justice officials regarding personality disorders, other root causes of criminal behavior, and the experience and needs of victims of crime is necessary in order for authorities in see beyond the law to consider the bigger picture that includes public safety and the common good.

Criminal justice reform is necessary to ensure that, according to the Canadian Charter of Rights and Freedoms, all persons have "the equal protection and equal benefit of the law without discrimination." That includes victims of crime and the public at large. Only then, can public confidence in the Canadian criminal justice system be restored.

Part Seven

Disruption in Health Care

Cautious, careful people always casting about to preserve their reputations can never affect a reform.
— Susan B. Anthony

Every reform needs examples more than advocates.
— Anonymous

Chapter Twenty-six

So how could people be taken in by someone so charming and convincing on one hand, and yet so deceitful and manipulative on the other?

The legend of Dr. Jekyll, and his alter ego, Mr. Hyde, comes to mind. John A. Sanford, a Jungian analyst and writer, explains this Robert Louis Stevenson tale of what happens when the shadow side of one's personality is not integrated into the whole.

> Henry Jekyll's fundamental mistake was his desire to escape the tension of the opposites within him ... he knew that he had a dual nature; he was aware that there was another one in him whose desires were counter to his more usual desires for the approbation of mankind. Had he enlarged his consciousness and carried the tension of the opposites within him, it would have led to the development of his personality; ... he would have been individuated. But Jekyll chose instead to try to escape this tension by means of the transforming drug, so that he could be both Jekyll and Hyde and have the pleasures and benefits of living out both sides of his personality without guilt or tension. For as Jekyll, it is worth noting, he felt no responsibility for Hyde. 'For it was Hyde, after all, and Hyde alone that was guilty,' he once declared.[53]

Startling reports of criminal behavior within the medical community in the past decade serve as stark reminders that the medical profession is not immune from evil and deceitful acts. Many, including physicians, expect and believe that physicians are good and trustworthy. These accounts tell of the consequences when a physician's darker side is repressed and denied. Not long after the Fairview incident, an editorial drew the attention of members of the Alberta Medical Association to examples of physicians' violations of the trust that is so readily placed in them. Case examples of murders by physicians were noted. [54]

One of those references was to British general practitioner, Dr. Harold Shipman, who was convicted in January 2000, and sentenced to life imprisonment for murdering fifteen of his patients. The story, reported in the Canadian edition of a British tabloid with the headline "EVIL BEYOND WORDS, quoted the sentencing judge:

---

[53] Ablow, Keith Russell, *Without Mercy: The shocking true story of a doctor who murdered,* St. Martin's, NY, 1994, p. 76.

[54] Alberta Medical Association, Editorial, "Our integrity is under siege, *Alberta Doctors' Digest,* March/April, 2000, p. 1-2.

> For your own evil and wicked purposes you grossly abused the trust that each of your victims placed in you. You were, after all, each victim's doctor ... You have not shown the slightest remorse or contrition for any of your evil deeds. And you have subjected the family and friends of each of your victims to the agony of having to relive the tragedy in court.[55]

Shipman was born in 1946 into a working class family in South Yorkshire. He was apparently a loner from an early age. His mother, who greatly influenced and encouraged him in his studies, died of cancer when he was 17 years of age. Although apparently shattered by her death, Shipman showed little outward signs of grief at the time. *The International Express* reported:

> Shipman was forever tormented by his mother's death. This, combined with his arrogance and a conviction that he was professionally superior to everyone else, underpinned a difficult personality... former colleagues tell of Shipman's massive mood swings, the pleasure he took in humiliating them in public and his inability to handle frustrations. They describe a man with a violent temper, bent on proving that he was best – a man who could not accept that he was wrong and who always wanted to be in control.[56]

One year after Shipman began general practice, he became addicted to drugs and was charged with three offences of obtaining a controlled drug by deception. He lost his job and attended a drug rehabilitation program. When Shipman was convicted of forging pethidine prescriptions in 1976, the judge recommended that Shipman not be allowed to prescribe drugs again. The General Medical Council was informed. Psychiatric reports said that Shipman would not likely relapse into drug dependency and that it would be good for him to continue general practice. Shipman's conviction was kept secret at the time.[57]

Shipman returned to general practice in 1977, this time in the town of Hyde. Dr. Linda Reynolds, who began work at the same surgery in September 1996, noted after a year that Dr. Shipman was present at the death of many of his patients. Some suggested that Shipman cared so much about his patients that he would often check on them at home, even without being called.

Reynolds, however, also noted the seemingly unusually high death rate among Shipman's patients. And there was a pattern. All were older women who lived alone and who were found dead by Shipman. In March 1998, an increasingly suspicious Reynolds con-

---

[55] *International Express*, February 8, p. 5.
[56] Ibid, p. 8.
[57] Ibid, p. 5.

tacted the police who investigated the report, but did not find adequate evidence to make a charge.

In June of that same year, Angela Woodruff, alarmed by the sudden death of her mother, was shocked to find that her mother's will had been forged, leaving her estate to Dr. Shipman. Woodruff, a solicitor, investigated further and reported her findings to the police. Police had Kathleen Gundy's body exhumed and learned that she had been given a massive dose of morphine. Even after Shipman's arrest, he "tried to bluster his way through police interviews."[58]

Further to the trial that convicted Shipman, an inquiry into the death of 450 patients who died under the care of Dr. Shipman began in June 2001. The *National Post* reported that "these staggering figures would make Dr. Shipman the most prolific serial killer of modern times ... even now, Hyde is divided over his guilt, with many people refusing to believe such a thing was possible."[59]

The Shipman case raises questions about how a physician could have managed to cover up his tracks for so long. He hid behind the façade of being a caring physician who went out of his way to see patients in their homes.

Wensley Clarkson, in his documentation of Shipman's story, notes that Shipman consistently denied charges against him and made up stories about what happened. For example, investigations revealed that Shipman added notes on his computerized client files to support the diagnosis that he wrote on his patients' death certificates. These entries were often made after the actual time of death. In his epilogue, Clarkson summarizes:

> What I hope my book has established is how Shipman got away for so long with his career of mass murder. . . . It surpasses belief that such systemic evil could flourish undetected and unchallenged for so long. The case of Fred Shipman has exposed a catastrophic failure in the British medical system. [60]

Clarkson notes that Shipman's crimes were about power and status. He identifies common denominators that apply to the "rogue, Fred Shipman-type killer doctor."

1. They do not usually start killing until middle age.

2. They abuse drugs, in particular diamorphine or its cognates.

3. They are brusque and acerbic in their manner.

---

[58] "Women whose bravery and persistence sprang the trap." *International Express*, February 8, 2000, p.9.

[59] The *National Post*, June 25, 2001.

[60] Clarkson, Wensley, *The Good Doctor*, St. Martin's Press, NY, 2002, p. 308.

4. They are arrogant with colleagues.

5. They can command extraordinary loyalty from those close to them.

6. Often self-made, they are over-conscious of their status as doctors.

7. They have a complete lack of empathy.[61]

Harold Shipman died after being found hanging in his cell in Wakefield Prison on January 13. 2004.

* * *

Best selling author James B. Stewart documents another appalling account of serial killings by a physician. In an intriguing piece of investigative reporting, Stewart chronicles the career of Michael Swango over the period of nearly twenty years in four American states; Illinois, Ohio, North Dakota, New York and Zimbabwe, Africa. During those years, Swango allegedly took the lives of at least thirty patients. Stewart suggests that Swango is "the first alleged serial killer in this century to have emerged in the guise of a physician." [62]

It is noteworthy that Swango and Shipman were both being brought to justice around the same time – Swango in the United States and Shipman in Britain.

In July 2000, Swango was charged with the murder of three patients in the Veterans Affairs Center in Northport, Long Island in 1993. Later that year, as part of a plea bargain, Swango pleaded guilty to killing four people, three men at the Veterans Affairs Hospital in New York and one woman at Ohio State University Hospital. In exchange for his guilty plea, Ohio would not seek the death penalty and Swango would not be extradited to Zimbabwe, where he was also suspected in patient deaths. He was sentenced to four sentences of life in prison without parole.[63]

Swango was born October 21, 1954 in Tacoma Washington. His father served in the Vietnam War and was away from home for prolonged periods. Swango, who served in the United States Marine Corps, was fascinated with war and violent death (according to later reports). He worked as a paramedic prior to entering Southern Illinois University Medical School and continued employment with the ambulance service while in medical school.

Concerned about Swango's attitude and lack of progress, some of Swango's medical classmates wrote to the Student Progress

---

[61] Ibid., p. 310-311.

[62] Stewart, James B., *Blind Eye*, Touchstone, NY, 2000, p. 295.

[63] "Swango admits to slaying", *The Columbus Dispatch*, October 19, 2000.

Committee expressing their view that he was not suitable to be a physician nor competent enough to be an intern. When questioned by the committee about a fabricated and plagiarized medical history and report, Swango denied the allegation. A unanimous vote by the committee was necessary to expel a student. Eight voted in favor, one abstained and one voted to give him another chance. The physician who defended Swango later admitted that he had made a mistake and that Swango's critics "were much more correct." He added, "I was wrong about him. I was duped."[64]

Swango was the model medical student during his last year in medical school and graduated one year later, in 1983.

Ohio State University accepted Swango into a neurosurgery residency upon the successful completion of his internship. Apparently it missed the warning in a Dean's letter from Southern Illinois University drawing attention to the medical school's concern about Swango's conduct and the need for him to repeat a rotation. [65]

When a patient had to be resuscitated after Swango reportedly injected something into her intravenous, he denied being in the room. When the Director of Nursing learned of the incident and the increase of mysterious deaths on the unit since Swango's arrival, she reported it to senior personnel at the hospital and university.

An investigation was carried out and while Swango was exonerated, physicians who worked with him were advised to observe him closely. There was no further inquiry nor were the police notified. The Director of Nursing was stunned by the lack of action by the hospital and university authorities, left the university, and later told Stewart: "The doctors did not want to believe. They were in denial." [66]

In early 1984, the Residency Review Committee, noting that Swango did not demonstrate the qualities required of a neurosurgeon, discontinued his residency but fearful of a lawsuit, allowed him to complete his internship. Swango was able to obtain positive recommendations that enabled him to be licensed in Ohio.[67]

He returned to his hometown, Quincy, Illinois, and was hired again by Adams County Ambulance Service. However, when it became evident that Swango was poisoning his colleagues on the ambulance team by slipping something into their food and drinks,

---

[64] Stewart, p. 312.
[65] Stewart, p. 59.
[66] Stewart, p. 311.
[67] Stewart, p. 88.

he was charged and convicted of six counts of aggravated battery and sentenced to five years in jail.

Following the trial, the Franklin County prosecutor in Ohio hired a homicide detective to work on the investigation in cooperation with the police, the medical board investigator, and Ohio State university and hospital personnel. No charges were laid, but the Ohio State Medical Board also investigated the suspicious activities by Swango at Ohio State University. Swango's license to practice medicine was suspended in both Ohio and Illinois in early 1986.

The ABC news program 20/20 aired an interview with Swango on February 13, 1986, the day after his Ohio license was suspended, and predictably Swango used the broadcast as an opportunity to claim his innocence.

He was released from prison on August 21,1987, changed his name, and in May 1991, applied for a position in West Virginia. As part of the application process, Swango had to reveal his own name. He provided forged documents to support his application and claimed that his Illinois license had been suspended because of a conviction relating to an altercation in a restaurant. When authorities in Illinois learned of Swango's attempt to cover up the truth, they sent copies of Swango's court orders to the chief of medicine of Ohio Valley Medical Center in West Virginia. Swango was not hired.

Undeterred however, in September 1991, Swango applied for a residency at the University of South Dakota in Sioux Falls, fabricating a story that he was a victim of a miscarriage of justice and that the charges against him were a result of jealousy by his colleagues that he was a physician. Only months into his residency, a segment of the earlier 20/20 broadcast of the prison interview with Swango was aired and the University of South Dakota quickly suspended him.

In the spring of 1993, Swango was persuasive enough to be accepted for a residency in psychiatry at the State University of New York on Long Island. The university did not check his professional history so did not know that Swango had lost his license in two states. He was later suspended when the school learned the truth about his background.

One year later, in October of 1994, a warrant was issued for Swango's arrest on charges of "defrauding a federal facility, the VA hospital, by gaining admission to the Stony Brook residency program on false pretenses."[68]

Swango was by then a fugitive, and his whereabouts were unknown to the police. One month later, Swango arrived in Zimbabwe, Africa to work as a physician at a Lutheran Mission Hospital in Mnene. Within months, there were suspicious deaths at the hospital and Swango was suspended in July 1995.

Swango moved on to another hospital in Zimbabwe where he convinced people he had been treated unfairly and was the victim of reverse discrimination against white doctors. A prominent lawyer agreed to represent him in a lawsuit against the Church.

When Swango was contacted by police for an interview, he left the country. He worked for a short time in Zambia and then traveled to Saudi Arabia. When forced to return to the United States in June 1997 to obtain a Saudi visa, Swango was arrested at O'Hare Airport in Chicago on charges of fraud. He pled guilty to the fraud charge and in June 1998, was sentenced to three and half years in prison. He was later charged and convicted of murder.

Stewart's detailed account of Swango's career describes the manipulative, deceitful behavior of a man who conned authorities into believing his lies, thus giving him access to patients for whom he had no regard. Without any sense of conscience, he used the tools of his profession to take their lives.

Two obvious questions arise. First, what motivated Swango's actions. Secondly, how could the authorities turn a blind eye to the danger that Swango posed for his patients, colleagues and friends?

Stewart notes that Swango had refused to be examined by a psychiatrist or psychologist. In an attempt to better understand Swango's behavior, Stewart contacted forensic psychologist, Dr. Jeffrey Smalldon, an expert on serial killers.

Although Swango fits the profile of a psychopath with narcissistic tendencies, Smalldon stressed that one ought not make such a diagnosis without seeing and properly assessing the individual.

'A psychopath is generally understood to be someone who lacks a capacity for empathy and may exhibit aggressive, perverted, criminal or amoral behavior. The psychopath tends to be highly self-absorbed. The condition is usually classified as an extreme and dangerous variation of narcissistic personality disorder, narcissism being the excessive love of self. But it is not a form of insanity: psychopaths

---

[68] Stewart, p. 224.

are fully aware of their actions, the actions' consequences, and can distinguish right from wrong.[69]

Dr. Joan Lang, Professor and Director of Residency Training, Department of Psychiatry, University of Texas Medical Branch concurs that Swango's story:

> could serve as a textbook illustration of a psychopath or sociopath in current terminology (The Diagnostic and Statistic Manual of Mental Disorders of the American Psychiatric Association), Antisocial Personality Disorder or APSD. Such individuals are characterized by displaying a pervasive pattern of disregard for and violation of the rights of others, failing to conform to social norms, deceitfulness, reckless disregard for the safety of self or others, consistent irresponsibility, and lack of remorse. Often, their own self-appraisal is arrogant and inflated.[70]

* * *

The Swango and Shipman stories remind us that there are folk who have no qualms about harming others and lying or distorting the truth for their own purposes.

Dr. Robert D. Hare, psychology professor emeritus at the University of British Columbia, confronted the problem of psychopathy in his research documented in the book, *Without Conscience*. Alerting us to the magnitude of the problem by pointing out that there are at least 2 million psychopaths in North America, Hare also states:

> not surprisingly, many psychopaths are criminals, but many others remain out of prison using their charm and chameleon like abilities to cut a wide swath through society and leaving a wake of ruined lives behind them.[71]

In groundbreaking research regarding the nature and roots of psychopathy, Hare developed the Psychopathy Checklist as a way of identifying those who fit the profile of this personality disorder. Hare's work has implications for all of us, as we are likely to come in contact with these persons and, as in the Swango story, fail to recognize the danger they pose to others.

Hare's work also has great significance for the criminal justice system. Proper assessment of offenders using the checklist ought to

---

[69] Stewart, p. 290.

[70] Parkridge Center for Health, Faith and Ethics, "Swango: the View from the Couch" *Religion and Ethics Newsweekly*, February 1998.

[71] Hare, Robert D., *Without Conscience: The Disturbing World of the Psychopaths Among Us*, Simon & Schuster, New York, N.Y, 1993, p. 2.

be a mandatory part of the criminal justice process especially at times of sentencing and consideration for parole. However, if character evidence of the accused person, who exhibits features of the psychopathic personality, is not admissible in the criminal trial, the court could be taken in and manipulated into believing lies.

Hare stresses that the Psychopathy Checklist is for professional use only and warns against using the list to diagnose oneself or others. However, it helps to be alert when key symptoms present as a pattern of behavior.

Emotional and interpersonal traits include being glib and superficial; egocentric and grandiose; displaying lack of remorse or guilt; having lack of empathy; being deceitful and manipulative; having shallow emotions. Symptoms of social deviance include impulsiveness, poor behavior controls, need for excitement, lack of responsibility, early behavior problems, and adult antisocial behavior. [72]

Hare provides "a survival guide" as to how to protect oneself from the devastating effects that a psychopath can have on one's life. He warns against being influenced by what he calls the props such as a "winning smile, the captivating body language, and the fast talk of the typical psychopath." He includes a description of the "intense, emotionless or 'predatory' stare" or the "empty eyes" of the psychopath. [73]

Indeed, it is difficult for those whose actions are motivated by their conscience and governed by a moral standard of honesty and integrity to believe that psychopaths live among us and can, apparently without conscience, so easily violate the trust that others place in them. Innocent, trusting folk are particularly vulnerable and likely to become the prey of the psychopath.

Hare warns:

> Don't wear blinkers. Enter new relationships with your eyes wide open. Like the rest of us most psychopathic con artists and "love thieves" initially hide their dark side by 'putting their best foot forward.' But they go further to exploit the axiom that social intercourse depends on trust, and that it is impossible for us to pay close and cynical attention to everything they say and do. Accordingly, they typically attempt to overwhelm their victims with flattery, feigned concern and kindness, and phony stories about financial dealings and social status. Cracks may soon begin to appear in the mask they wear, but once you are trapped in their web of deceit and control, it will be difficult to escape financially and emotionally unscathed. [74]

---

[72] Hare, p. 34.

[73] Hare, p. 208.

[74] Hare, p. 211.

Indeed, Hare's warning could be addressed directly to the health care community where care is contingent not only on competence, but also on the trustworthiness and integrity of the health professional. Those in authority are charged with the identification and confrontation of those who put both clients and colleagues at risk when they violate the trust placed in them.

Stewart notes that the incidence of serial killing is increasing and that over half of the cases of serial killing in the United States have happened since 1970. In the final chapter of *Blind Eye*, Stewart writes:

> There seems to be little doubt among experts that serial killing is a socially influenced phenomenon, and that one instance with its attendant publicity encourages emulation, especially on the part of grandiose, narcissistic personalities determined to generate a blaze of publicity for themselves.[75]

Recent school and workplace killings in both Canada and the United States could well be the stimulus for other similar actions. Stewart's observation is consistent with that of Richard Rohr, a modern theologian, who writes,

> Many of our social institutions, particularly, government, law, education, the Church, the military, family and marriage have been soundly discredited in the last fifty years. Each one is its own sad story of lost authority and focus. Unfortunately, this leaves the media and the business world to communicate daily meaning for most people! Now that is scary-and probably this is the first time in human history that we have tried to carry society on two such tiny and fragile shoulders. It is certain to produce fragile people and a very unstable society. [76]

It should be noted that Rohr's observation was made prior to the Enron and Nortel scandals. Does that mean that the media might now be the only remaining authority from which many people draw meaning? If so, what is the impact of the violent images that bombard us through the media?

Principles of truth, respect and care for one another, core values of our societal institutions, have been replaced by an emphasis on the rights and the interests of the individual at the expense of community and the common good. The legal system has become the medium for exercising and ensuring those rights, thus opening the way for persons who have no regard for others to exploit the system and other people in order to further their own interests.

---

[75] Stewart. P. 295.

[76] Rohr, Richard with John Bookser Feister, *Hope Against Darkness*, St. Anthony Messenger Press, Cincinnati, 2001, p. 45.

As a result of the overriding possibility of litigation, professional regulatory authorities are compromised in their duty to maintain professional standards and ethics. The behavior of professionals may be motivated more by extrinsic factors, such as economics, fear of litigation or loss of image, than moral obligation and service of others. Strong leadership is required to take a stand on matters that compromise professional integrity and the well being of the public at large.

* * *

A Canadian case is another poignant example of breakdowns in the exchange of information between physician licensing jurisdictions. Richard Neale, trained in Britain as a gynecologist, lost his operating privileges in British Columbia in 1979 after a botched surgery resulted in a patient death. The B.C. College of Physicians and Surgeons ordered him to undergo retraining. He chose to move to Ontario where he lost his license in 1985 after a 1981 incident of malpractice that also resulted in the patient's death.

By that time, Neale was practising in Britain. When British authorities were alerted, they did not act until further unfortunate incidents occurred. The British General Medical Council stripped Neale of his license in 2000 after finding him guilty of "incompetence, operating without consent, carrying out unnecessary procedures, failing to monitor patients postoperatively and duping a patient into paying for private surgery." In spite of the huge number of women complaining about his treatment, Neale pleaded for another chance.[77]

A W5 report on CTV in early 2001 reported that 40 of Neale's former patients were calling for a criminal investigation of Neale. They questioned why this was allowed to happen and demanded an apology from the medical authorities.

Following a police investigation, Richard Neale was finally arrested in January 2006, and faces criminal charges in Britain.

* * *

The Cooper case in Alberta is yet another example of how a physician was able to move from one jurisdiction to another, apparently without full disclosure of his history. In a special report by Jim

---

[77] *Canadian Medical Association Journal*, 2000; 163(5): 584.

Farrell of the *Edmonton Journal* on October 7, 2000, the day following Cooper's conviction, his story was made public.

Abraham Cooper is the youngest son of a Mennonite laborer who was unable to work because of poor health. When his father died, Abe's mother remarried and took Abe with her to live on a farm in another community. Cooper's stepfather was a strict religious man who apparently ruled with an iron fist. Cooper rebelled and ran away from home for the second time at the age of sixteen.

At some point he changed his Mennonite name of Koop to Cooper, and joined the army where he became a second lieutenant and administration officer in the medical corps. Cooper married while overseas in Germany and on his return to Canada, enrolled in university and medical school, graduating in 1973.

A note in the medical school yearbook reads, "Abe is noted for his shaves, shines and short hair ... He has kept classmates amused with his army anecdotes and obscene gestures (usually done simultaneously)."

After fulfilling his commitment to the army with three years of service at the Canadian Forces Base in Calgary, Cooper moved to the United States where he practiced as a small town country doctor from 1980 to 1988. He worked briefly in small towns in Montana before moving to North Dakota for three years.

Commenting on Cooper's difficulty in getting along with the nurses, a retired physician from Glasgow, Montana, stated, "Some of the nurses didn't like him and some detested him. They couldn't put their fingers on it, though. It just seemed you were never meeting the real guy." Neither were the physicians impressed, it seemed, with Cooper's competence as a physician.

Cooper moved on to Hallock, Minnesota, where before long he was involved in a dispute with one of the town's senior doctors who Cooper reported to the State Medical Board. Incidents involving angry outbursts by Cooper claiming other doctors were stealing his patients (episodes similar to those later reported in Fairview) had also occurred at the Hallock Hospital.

One physician stated, "We didn't change him. We just passed him on. You see his trail of destruction." Cooper was apparently able to move from one community to another because he was given glowing letters of reference. A classmate of Cooper's told the *Journal*:

Letters like that should never be trusted. They're usually part of a deal struck by medical authorities who want to push a doctor out the door; leave quietly and we'll help you find another job ... What happens with letters of reference is that no one wants to put themselves on a limb because what happens is that a doctor will turn around and file a lawsuit.[78]

That is what happened in Fairview when the hospital authorities boldly stood up to Cooper and refused to accept his disruptive behavior. The tragic consequences indicate that the fear expressed by authorities in the earlier cases was well founded.

What will the response be to this tragedy? Will physicians, other health professionals, licensing bodies and health authorities be even more reluctant to "put themselves on a limb" and choose to remain silent?

Or will the authorities be quicker to respond to the warning signs, more vigilant in monitoring attitudes and behaviors, less reticent to take action and more diligent to ensure that other appropriate jurisdictions are aware of matters that could put patients, colleagues and the public at risk? Will they have their eyes wide open so as not to become complacent and be taken in?

---

[78] "A doctor's life long quest—-for stature", *Edmonton Journal*, October 7, 2000, A2-3.

Chapter Twenty-seven

So what did go wrong? How could a situation that was jeopardizing patient care, staff safety and morale at the Fairview Health Complex have led to accusations of conspiracy, lawsuits and the desperate act of killing?

Could something more have been done to redirect the allegations and threats toward constructive change? Ought the conflict have been referred to a mediator trained in conflict resolution and would it have made a difference? Should the vicious backlash have been expected or could it have been prevented?

In ordinary circumstances, it would be reasonable to expect a willingness to work together to review issues and resolve differences in the best interests of all involved. However, this was far from being an ordinary situation.

Problems had been identified and recommendations were implemented. Cooper who was identified consistently as a disruptive presence and primary source of the difficulties, refused to take responsibility for his actions. His hospital privileges were not renewed when he refused to sign the Code of Conduct. Even then, he did not change.

Cooper carried on his medical practice in the community and continued to promote distrust within and outside of the medical and health care community. He used the legal system to support his cause. His repeated appeals, his lawsuits against his medical colleagues and the hospital board, topped off with threats of lawsuits against anyone who dared to challenge him, held innocent people hostage.

Some would have liked to bring the whole story into the open but were prevented from doing so because of the legal actions against them. Thus, Cooper maintained control and was able to convince some members of the community that he was the victim of unfair treatment. Cooper's actions and tactics violated the Canadian Medical Association Code of Ethics for physicians.

The Code (1996 version) states that physicians should:

Recognize that the self-regulation of the profession is a privilege and that each physician has a continuing responsibility to merit this privilege;

Avoid impugning the reputation of colleagues for personal motives, however, report to the appropriate authority any unprofessional conduct by colleagues;

Collaborate with other physicians and health professionals in the care of patients and the functioning and improvement of health services;

Seek help from colleagues and appropriately qualified professionals for personal problems that adversely affect your service to patients, society or the profession.

There is a difference between reporting unprofessional conduct in order to ensure safe, ethical professional practice for patients, and making allegations in order to undermine a colleague's practice and reputation. Reports of the various investigations and the lawsuit itself demonstrate Cooper's continuing attempts to malign and impugn his colleagues in order to clear himself and to recover his financial losses – losses that were a direct consequence of his own behavior.

Cooper was unwilling to collaborate with his medical colleagues and other health professionals. While he persisted in his accusations and claims that he was in fact the "whistleblower" regarding problems in the system, the evidence shows that his actions were more destructive than helpful in improving health services.

Cooper evidently made no attempt to comply with the professional code by seeking help in accepting responsibility or changing his behavior – behavior that was clearly affecting his service to patients and the medical profession. Reports concluded that Cooper's difficulty in getting along with other physicians was due to his inability to cooperate.

A Chief of Staff without authority to insist on assessment or treatment of a colleague faces a dilemma when signs of trouble are apparent. While sitting through the examinations for discovery relating to the lawsuit, Doug wrote in his notes,

I privately strongly counseled Cooper to talk to a friend, colleague about how he (Cooper) felt. I could not understand that a physician would not understand what we (our medical staff) were trying to do.... I did wish the College Registrar to talk to Cooper – like going to the principal in school. The complaints were not serious enough to make it 'the line in sand' fight.

Neither of Doug's suggestions was acted upon.

The College of Physician of Surgeons has a protocol for monitoring 'impaired physicians'; that is, physicians impaired by alcohol, drugs or mental illness.Doug was monitored in his recovery following treatment for substance abuse. Yet, Cooper, whose behavior was the source of significant problems, was neither assessed nor monitored.

Did the profession ever consider that Cooper's behavior was a sign of impairment that jeopardized his ability to provide professional and ethical medical care? His denial of responsibility, expressions of paranoia, projection and counterattacks on others were indicators that something was very wrong.

Having adopted the term "disruptive behavior" to describe such conduct, the medical profession now recognizes the problem as an urgent professional issue requiring attention. But by its very nature, disruptive behavior is elusive and resists being named or confronted. It requires assessment and intervention by skilled professionals with knowledge and understanding of the phenomenon.

Dr. Michael Glendel, a psychiatrist with an interest in physician health writes:

> Disruptive physicians pose special problems. ... Often such doctors deny to themselves or to others the wrongful nature of their actions. They need to externalize responsibility ... by blaming co-workers, administrators, working conditions, patients or other events. They resist effective confrontation by setting up covert threats of retaliation or even self-harm. They may covertly use their powerful positions or personalities to silence perceived criticism. They resist the monitoring of their behavior by challenging the authority of those who order it and by finding loopholes in the behavioral requirements.[79]

Protocols for managing disruptive behavior have now been developed. Dr. Michael Kaufmann of the Ontario Medical Association Physician Health program describes a process beginning with confrontation that expects immediate change in behavior. He adds:

> Acknowledgement of the behavioral problem by the physician should be sought, along with his or her responsibility to take corrective action. Acceptable outcomes should be defined. Any support required to reach these outcomes (possibly including cost of assessment and/or treatment) should be offered.

---

[79] Glendel, Michael H., "Disruptive Behaviors, Personality Problems, and Boundary Violations", *The Handbook of Physician Health* edited by Harry S. Goldman, Michael Myers and Leah Dickstein, American Medical Association, 2000, p.143.

Contingencies, which may affect a doctor's privileges or involve the regulatory authorities must be seriously considered if the doctor is not compliant with the process.[80]

The Alberta College of Physicians and Surgeons did appoint physicians to investigate difficulties in the Fairview Health Complex, but even when reports consistently pointed to Cooper as being a disruptive presence, the College did not call for follow up with a clinical assessment or any disciplinary action. The Hospital Board was left to address the problem on its own, and then its members and the local physicians faced the backlash.

One continues to wonder what was going on within the system that had the mandate to regulate physician conduct. Surely, it was well aware of the problems. But why did the College of Physicians and Surgeons of Alberta not intervene with its full authority?

Perhaps complaints were minimized or dismissed because of the perception that "Fairview was always complaining" and that "Anyways, the situation there was dysfunctional."

Perhaps, it was because Fairview is a small, seemingly insignificant town in the North and there were more important issues demanding the attention of the authorities – or so they thought. Perhaps the College of Physicians and Surgeons feared facing litigation itself. Or perhaps the College did not in fact have the full authority to intervene and other rules or laws overrode its regulatory powers.

When physicians appealed for help, the College maintained that it did not receive complaints from physicians about physicians. Its role was to protect the public and so accepted only complaints from the public. But ought not hospital employees and physicians have had the same rights to protection as other citizens? Besides, wouldn't health professionals have the interests of the public in mind?

It would appear the College backed off from confronting Cooper directly about his conduct. There are some who would say that it failed in fulfilling its mandate. Yes, in the end, after waiting for the criminal justice system to complete its course and ensuring due process, the College did erase Cooper's license because of his manslaughter conviction.

Its related press release on January 13, 2004 stated:

> The conviction of manslaughter is a criminal offence and is obviously unbecoming to a member of the medical profession.

---

[80] Kaufmann, Michael, "Recognition and Management of the Behaviorally Disruptive Physician", *Ontario Medical Review*, April 2001, p. 55.

No mention at all was made of Cooper's long history of disruptive behavior.

The following month, Registrar Robert Burns reported to College members that the unprecedented press release had been issued in the interest of transparency. He cited a quote from Janice Stein in *The Cult of Efficiency*: "Self regulation by the profession is simply not working well enough, because it is not transparent enough."[81]

Burns, College registrar since 2002, was not part of the history leading up to the act of killing by a College member. Apparently for him, simply reporting the disciplinary action was transparent enough. However, true transparency would have revealed how Cooper had disrupted the Fairview health care community for years prior to taking another physician's life. Such a step would have conveyed the magnitude of the situation and given a strong message to physicians and the public that disruptive behavior can have disastrous consequences and should not and would not be tolerated.

A footnote in Stein's book refers to an investigation of the Ontario College of Physicians and Surgeons system of accountability. The report revealed that 99% of complaints in a six-year period were dismissed or handled in secrecy. It noted that doctors were placed on "a higher legal footing than complainants."[82]

Burns advised College members that change was in store with the new Health Professions Act that will legislate increased transparency of the complaints and discipline process. The culture of secrecy and self-regulation will, no doubt, be required to change.

The College Council and Burns did take steps to begin to address the problem of disruptive behavior of physicians. The new goal statements for the College of Physicians and Surgeons of Alberta reflect a commitment to professionalism and accountability.[83]

Often citing legal reasons, the College continues to avoid the topic when it comes down to the Cooper case. It does not acknowledge publicly that it failed in its duty to ensure that Cooper was fit to practise medicine – even though there might have been some in the system who privately felt and thought otherwise.

While individuals have informally and unofficially acknowledged their regret for what has happened, the College has not made

---

[81] "Registrar's Report", *The Messenger*, Feb 2004, Issue 108,College of Physicians and Surgeons of Alberta, p. 3.

[82] Stein, Janice, *The Cult of Efficiency*, House of Anansi, 2003, p. 273.

[83] *The Messenger*, May 2005, CPSA, p. 4.

any formal statement about the tragic death of its member, Dr. Douglas George Snider, who, in effect, was killed in the line of duty.

The chair of the Physicians' Continuing Care Committee that had monitored Doug's recovery on behalf of the College was allowed to testify for the defence as an expert witness regarding alcoholism. When the appropriateness of this decision was questioned, given the potential for violation of confidentiality of the monitoring function, the College defended its position with the argument that one of its members (Cooper) was on trial. Doug, dead and no longer a member of the College, apparently didn't have the same right to 'representation' or protection by the licensing body.

Whatever the case, whatever happened or didn't happen, the stark truth is that a life has been lost and many other lives traumatized and changed forever.

The time has come for the medical community to take stock of its responses to reports of difficult behavior on the part of physicians. It is time to adopt a zero tolerance approach to abusive and disruptive behavior. Surely, the matter deserves the same kind of attention as is given to substance abuse. And hopefully, as the public demands to be informed, these matters will come to public attention sooner.

The health boards in Fairview demonstrated great courage in addressing the problem of disruptive behavior when it presented itself. They could have just as easily dismissed or ignored the problems. Indeed, given the disastrous outcome, some may wonder if it was worth it all.

It is now time to look ahead.

Unfortunately, incidents of violence in schools and the workplace are happening all too frequently. A common reaction is shock and dismay that such a thing could happen in that particular place or be perpetrated by that particular person. Often when the history of the incident and the story of the key players are reviewed, the warning signs of the tragedy were, in retrospect, there for all to see. Naturally, those involved then feel guilt and remorse that they hadn't recognized the problem and done something or enough to prevent the ensuing tragedy.

In an effort to raise awareness and ensure that the medical system learned from my brother's death, I presented a paper at the Physician Health Conference sponsored by the American and

Canadian Medical Associations in 2002. My paper included specific recommendations for change in the manner in which medical regulatory bodies address the problem of disruptive behavior by physicians.[84]

Although unable to right the wrong that was done, we can advocate for change and insist that the relevant systems take action so that such tragedies can be prevented in the future. Our family is seeking such a legacy for our loved one.

---

[84] See Appendix IV, page 180.

Chapter Twenty-eight

How has the medical profession responded? Has any progress been made in addressing disruptive workplace behavior in the health care setting or any other workplace for that matter?

Yes, Canadian medical authorities are taking steps to address the issue of disruptive conduct by physicians, and more generally, workplace bullying is now recognized as a threat to employee health and safety in any work setting.

The first step is to acknowledge the nature and extent of the problem. In May 2001, the University of Alberta commissioned a work and study environment review of the Faculty of Medicine and Dentistry. The study team reported:

> Within the institution, but not authorized by the institution, there exist pockets of intimidation, harassment and discrimination and breaches of employment conditions. [85]

In November 2002, the Dean, Dr. Lorne Tyrrell, announced the creation of an office of Equity and Faculty Development to address these matters, beginning with a Code of Conduct. Professional assistance in conflict resolution is now available and concerns about unprofessional conduct can be addressed openly and constructively.

Relationships of trust and respectful communication between physicians and other members of the health care team are critical for effective team work and quality health care. An article in *The Physician Executive* reviews the results of a study examining specifically the impact of nurse-physician relationships on nurse satisfaction and retention.[86]

On the average, nurses rated the importance of disruptive behavior as a factor affecting their job satisfaction and morale as 8.01 on a scale of 1 to 10. Reported disruptive behavior took the forms of disrespect, berating colleagues, use of abusive language and condescending behavior. The physician authors bring the matter to the attention of their medical colleagues and suggest several approaches to improve nurse physician relationships. They note that

---

[85] Report of Faculty of Medicine and Dentistry Work and Study Environment Review, November 2002. *www.med.ualberta.ca.* p.13.

[86] Rosenstein, A., Russell, H. and Lauve, R,. "Disruptive Physician Behavior Contributes to Nursing Shortage", *The Physician Executive*, November/December 2002, 8-11. Note that the study "Nurse-Physician Relationships: Impact on Nurse Satisfaction and Retention" was originally reported in the *American Journal of Nursing*, June 2002.

change is most likely to happen when a "physician champion embraces the issue and spreads the word to colleagues."[87]

At its annual meeting in June 2004, the Confederation of Medical Licensing Authorities of Canada (FMLAC) addressed this matter in an educational session entitled, "Physicians with Disruptive Behaviors – can something really be done for them and about them?"

The objectives of the session, chaired by Dr. Karen Shaw, Deputy Registrar of the College of Physicians and Surgeons of Saskatchewan, were:

1. To review the current work of the College of Physicians and Surgeons of Ontario on this issue.
2. To examine the various components of a proposed systemic response to this problem.
3. To create linkages with professionalism and highlight the challenges inherent with a system of self- or profession-led regulation.

Dr. Graeme Cunningham, who brought this issue forward as a priority during his presidency of the Council of the College of Physicians and Surgeons of Ontario (CPSO) in 2003, provided an overview of the problem.

He noted that nurses were the first to identify difficulty with disruptive behavior by physicians – a topic that did not appear in the medical literature until the 1990's. Difficult behavior once tolerated is no longer acceptable.

The Ontario initiative was based on the realization that complaints about physicians fell into four categories. The College had a method for addressing matters pertaining to standards, incompetence or incapacity but no program existed for "physicians who are ungovernable, un-remediable, nasty, or otherwise disruptive."

Participants at a CPSO multi stakeholder workshop in 2003 committed to continue working together to create a collaborative, systemic response to the problem of disruptive behavior by physicians. The following definition of the disruptive physician was accepted at the Ontario workshop: "A physician who cannot, or will not function well with others to the extent that his or her behavior, by words or actions, has the potential to interfere with quality health care delivery."

The FMLAC meeting in 2004 featured a panel that reviewed the components of a systemic response to the issue. These included communications and policy development, educational/mentor-

---

[87] Ibid, p. 11.

ing/role modeling, physician health, and institutional and regulatory responses. I attended the meeting and was given an opportunity to speak from a public/family perspective.[88]

Dr. Dennis Kendel, Registrar of the College of Physicians and Surgeons of Saskatchewan, speaking from the point of view of the regulatory authority, was clear in his position that medical regulatory authorities ought to have explicit policy and response strategies. Disruptive physician behavior, Kendel believes, is damaging to the profession's image, its working relationship with other health care personnel and has real potential to erode the quality and safety of care provided to patients.

Kendel noted that Medical Regulatory Authorities have the "authority, moral responsibility and capacity to 'set the tone' for a systemic response, to help build capacity for early detection and intervention and to 'backstop' local regulatory mechanisms with its statutory authority when local mechanisms fail."

He called on his colleagues to "bring the issue out of the shadows and foster candid discussion within the profession and within health care workplaces." He suggested that the profession respond to disruptive physician behavior with strategies similar to those used to address physician chemical impairment.

Sarah Hutchison described the role of the Ontario Medical Association Physician Health Program in addressing disruptive physician behavior. The article by Dr. Michael Kaufmann, the Medical Director of the AMA Physician Health Program, reviewing the forms and causes of disruptive behavior and the importance of clinical evaluation and differential diagnosis, was distributed at the conference.

According to Kaufmann, disruptive behavior may be the inappropriate expression of anger by abusive language, throwing of objects or personal threats or:

> may simply take the form of lack of cooperation with others. Replies to pages may be late or ignored. Committee or other hospital duties may be neglected-with haughty contempt or passive aggressive avoidance.... Contrary positions taken by colleagues or superiors may cause resentment, resulting in the threat of retribution, litigation, or even violence. [89]

---

[88] My presentation included recommendations for reform in the regulatory management of disruptive behavior by physicians. See Appendix IV, page 179.

[89] Kaufmann, Michael, "Recognition and Management of the Behaviorally Disruptive Physician", *The Ontario Medical Review*, April 2003, p. 53.

Ruling out other mental health or substance abuse problems, physicians displaying disruptive behavior often present with personality problems.

Kaufmann elaborates:

> These physicians behave in ways consistent with life-long maladaptive patterns. It is unusual for such a physician to experience insight as to how his or her behavior affects others. It therefore falls to administrators, regulators and others in positions of responsibility to determine when and how remedial action should be taken.[90]

Kaufmann's most current article describes a staged rehabilitative approach to the management of disruptive behavior. A flowchart maps the process of evaluation and assessment, treatment and recommendations that follow a referral to the Ontario Physician Health Program.[91]

A Canadian Medical Association course on physician health is now being offered to physician leaders across Canada. Dr. Kaufmann teaches a section on the management of disruptive behavior in physicians. The matter is also addressed in a recent article by the director of the Physician and Family Support Program of the Alberta Medical Association.[92]

Disruptive, intimidating behavior might also be referred to as bullying. The term is now beginning to be used in the Canadian medical literature. The Canadian medical newspaper, the *Medical Post*, addressed the issue of disruptive behavior by physicians in an article entitled, "Dealing with the Hospital Bully," [93]

Workplace bullying and violence is now recognized internationally as a threat to employee productivity, health and safety. At one time, bullying was primarily associated with the schoolyard. However, researchers and writers are now reporting on this phenomenon in the workplace.

Prompted by a series of incidents of rage in North American schoolyards and workplaces, Gerry Smith, manager of a National Trauma Response Service, wrote the book, *Work Rage*. It discusses both the problems and solutions and ways to prevent and lessen the impact of violence in the workplace. Smith notes that:

---

[90] Ibid, p.54.

[91] Kaufmann, Michael, "Management of Disruptive Behavior in Physicians: A staged, rehabilitative approach", *The Ontario Medical Review*, October 2005, p. 59.

[92] Maier, Dianne B., "Disruptive? A Physician? The medicine can be simple", *Alberta Doctors' Digest*, Sept/Oct 2005.

[93] Gautam, Manta, Helping Hand Column, *Medical Post*, April 27, 2004.

> The impact of trauma on victims, witnesses and communities at large is vastly underestimated, and this is particularly true in the event of tragedy resulting from rage and violence.[94]

In follow-up to the recommendations of a coroner's inquest into the 1999 shooting rampage resulting in the death of five persons at O.C. Transpo in Ottawa, the Canada Safety Council called for legislation to prevent workplace violence and workplace policies to address violence and harassment.

In June 2004, a new law to address psychological harassment came into effect in Quebec. It addresses the more covert forms of violence in the workplace such as insults, intimidation and sabotage (backstabbing). While more difficult to profile than overt physical assault, psychological harassment is an invisible form of bullying that wears down targets who feel helpless, fearful and shameful, often not sure why they are being victimized.

The Quebec law defines psychological harassment as:

> any vexatious behavior in the form of repeated and hostile or unwanted conduct, verbal comments, actions or gestures that affect an employee's dignity or psychological or physical integrity and that results in a harmful work environment for the employee.[95]

Andrea Adams, a British journalist and author is credited with bringing public attention to workplace bullying in 1992. Four years later, Tim Field, himself a target of bullying, begins his book, *Bully in Sight*, with an acknowledgement of Adams work.

Field describes bullying this way:

> Bullying occurs when one person, (typically but not necessarily) in a position of power, authority, trust, responsibility, management feels threatened by another person usually (but not always) a subordinate who is displaying qualities of ability, popularity, knowledge, skill, strength, drive, determination, tenacity, success, etc. ...[96]

In 1998, Drs Ruth and Gary Namie, therapists, researchers and authors of *The Bully at Work*, founded the Workplace Bullying and Trauma Institute (WPTI) in Bellingham, Washington, U.S.A. Commited to "exposing the silent epidemic", the Institute focuses on education and research.[97]

---

[94] Smith, Gerry, *Work Rage*, Harper Collins, Toronto, 2000, p. 21.

[95] "Targeting Workplace Bullies", Canada Safety Council. 2004, *www.safety-council.org* .

[96] Field, Tim, *Bully in Sight*, Wessex, Oxfordshire, 1996, p. xxiii. *www.bullyonline.org*.

[97] Namie, G. & Namie, R., *The Bully at Work*, 2nd ed., Sourcebooks, Naperville, Illinois, 2003. *www.bullyinginstitute.org*.

Dr. Gary Namie sums up the heart of the issue this way:

The characteristic common to all bullies is that they are controlling competitors who exploit their cooperative targets. Most bullies would stop if the rules changed and bullying was punished.[98]

Bullying is a sytemic problem that demands a systemic solution. It disrupts and undermines trust in the workplace and ought not be tolerated. Workplace morale and relationships thrive when the principles of **respect, trust, truth** and **accountability** are validated and enforced by all relevant stakeholders.

---

[98] Namie, Gary, "Workplace Bullying: Escalated Incivility", *Ivey Business Journal*, Nov/Dec 2003, p.3.

Epilogue

The Doctor's Legacy

Lives of great men all remind us
We can make our lives sublime,
And, departing, leave behind us
Footprints on the sands of time.

– Henry Wadsworth Longfellow

Chapter Twenty-nine

So how is Dr. Douglas George (Schattschneider) Snider remembered?

In May 1999, while Fairview residents were searching for Doug, three women from the community gathered a collection of tributes and notes of thanks from the people of the Fairview area to Doug and his family. The collection was presented to his family with the following introduction:

> Dr. Snider was a great man. His life work and the many lives he touched was overwhelming to those of us who had the privilege of working on this book. As we read the entries herein, we are reminded of how fortunate we were to have known Doug as a friend, how blessed were to have had him as our physician, and how thankful we are to each of you for allowing your husband and father to dedicate his life to us, the residents of Fairview.
>
> We realized as we worked on these albums that the depth of Dr. Doug's compassion to the many people was not only unknown to those who knew him, but probably he himself did not realize just how many lives he had touched.
>
> So, your 'family and friends' of Fairview, Alberta, thank each of you and especially our thanks to Dr. Doug Snider. His memory will live on in each of you.[99]

One tribute, written by Kim Ruether, X-ray therapist at the Fairview Hospital began with a toast:

> Remember that love will win through
> And now a toast from me to you.
> Admiration for a physician and a friend,
> The respect for a person who gave to the end.
> You helped us through strife, dealt with unrest.
> You truly have given you very best.

Others used the words of Ralph Waldo Emerson to describe Doug.

> To laugh often and love much,
>
> To win the respect of intelligent people and the affection of children,
>
> To earn the appreciation of honest critics and endure the betrayal of false friends.

---

[99] This book of memories, collated by Sharon Bloom, Kay Helfrich and Lisa Spring, will be treasured by the Snider family for generations.

To appreciate beauty,
To find the best in others
To leave the world a better place.

Whether by a healthy child, a garden patch or a redeemed social condition:
To know even one life has breathed easier because you have lived.
This is to have succeeded.

The staff at the Fairview Health Complex have remembered Doug on the anniversary of his death by placing a wreath of flowers in the hospital entrance in his memory.

Photo: T. Klaepatch

In June 2003, the Fairview Health Complex Telehealth Conference Room was dedicated "In memory of a colleague and friend". It is a fitting reminder of Doug's dedicated service in Fairview and his commitment to teamwork and continuous learning.

In April 2004, when staff at the Fairview Health Complex nominated Doug for the Alberta Medical Association Medal for Distinguished Service, they wrote the following tribute:

> We affectionately remember Dr. Snider as a gentle spirit approachable by all. As colleagues, we felt supported, our professional judgment accepted and encouraged. With Dr. Snider, we enjoyed a comradery; we could tease, laugh and cry together. We could deal with acute cardiac situations, labor and delivery, psychological crisis, pediatric events and perform minor surgeries with competence.
>
> He understood physical health was only one factor in caring for the whole person, and adopted a holistic approach, acknowledging the spiritual and psychosocial aspects. Dr. Snider retained that educator side of him and enjoyed sharing information whether it came from reading a medical journal, a course, or previous experience, eager to take opportunities for professional growth.
>
> Dr. Snider was community minded, and took an interest in local and federal politics. Always looking for cost effective and practical solutions. He was a man who gave his all and his enthusiasm could be quite contagious.
>
> Proud of his four children and grandchildren, time was a precious commodity his family graciously shared. Being a rural physician, he was at the services of the community even when off duty and was a ready consultant for the neighboring nurse practitioner.
>
> We remember a ready smile, a speed walker with his tie flying off to the side or tucked securely between the buttons of his shirt. His admission to being a 'Type A' personality, who often thought faster than he could talk. We remember the twinkle in his eye, when he was matchmaker, he would state, 'everyone needs someone to love and hug.' We remember Dr. Snider's sense of humor and the giggle that would accompany a humorous tale. We remember a humble man often telling stories on himself. He was an encourager and supporter, one that instilled confidence in others.
>
> Although it was a different time, with a different organizational culture, Dr. Snider accepted a leading role always believing conflicts could be resolved with optimum benefits possible for all. We recognize that Dr. Snider empowered others to strive for excellence in his challenging and continually changing community setting and has left a lasting legacy.
>
> It was truly an honor and privilege to have known him.

In a letter I received from Doug in 1994, he shared a thought for the day: "Fortunate are the people whose roots are deep."

Doug's roots sustained him during trying times while he was alive and now continue to sustain our family. I address the following letter to my family and to all those who personally knew Doug and have been touched by his life and his death.

> For those of us who knew and loved Doug, the horror of the events of May 5, 1999 and the aftermath of that day has brought us together in a unique way. Doug will always be in our hearts. As we share our memories of a son, brother, husband, father, grandfather, uncle, cousin, son-in-law, brother-in-law, colleague, friend, family doctor, we give thanks for his life and the good times we shared.

> In the words of Grandpa Schattschneider, who even when grieving the tragic loss of his son, looked for something positive, "We've had a hard time; we'll never get over it but we have to remember the good times." We have been given courage and grace to face our pain and grief. We will likely continue to struggle, each in our own way, with the events surrounding Doug's death.

> We search for meaning and hope for constructive change as a result of this tragedy and injustice, but know that our lives will never be the same. Our challenge is to find a way to move on – not to forget what happened, but that our hurt and loss will be transformed into love and creative action.

> Above all, we have learned from the example of a man whose life and calling was *a matter of conscience*. That is Doug's legacy to all of us.

> Doug will be remembered for his passion for his family, his profession and his community...a love that will live on through his family and the lives that he touched. We pray for God's continued blessing on him as he lives on in our hearts and memories.

Love does not delight in evil but rejoices with the truth.
It always protects, always trusts, always hopes,
always perseveres...
And now these three remain; faith, hope and love.
But the greatest of these is love.

           – I Corinthians, 13: 6,7,13. (NIV)

The light shines in the darkness,
and the darkness has not overcome it.
— John 1:5 (RSV)

Appendices

Appendix I

Schattschneider Family Tree

George August
Schattschneider
1911-2004

Sophie Pubantz
1912-1972

Married April 19, 1934

Hazel Joan
(m. Lloyd Magnussen)

Douglas George
1939-1999
(m. Jean Ruth Pahal 1960)
Family name changed from
Schattschneider to Snider 1966

Mary Elizabeth
(m. Arthur Lange)

Brenda Mary
(m. Dale Zimmerman)
Sara Marie

Douglas Dean
(m. Kimber Knutson)
Jacqueline Lee

Grant Douglas
(1961-1993)

William Arthur
(m. Rhonda L'Estrange)

Daena Lee
(m. Gary Williams)
Douglas Carl
Brianna Rose

Darren George
(m. Mavis Anderson)
Benjamin Fenton
Cameron Douglas

Ernest George

Edward Frederick
(m. Shari Bartz)
Connor Edward
Braden Jesse
Sheldon Matthew

Appendix II

What I have learned about the criminal justice process

1) Our criminal justice system is more about the interpretation of the law than it is about truth and justice.

2) The Crown prosecutor represents the state – not the victim of the crime. The victim does not have an advocate in the criminal trial.

3) The accused is innocent until proven guilty beyond a reasonable doubt.

4) While many in the system treat the crime victim with respect, the mindset of the court is that the victim is an outsider.

5) The due process rights of the accused over ride the rights and dignity of the crime victim – the defense lawyer is given great latitude in exercising those rights even if it means revictimizing and putting the victim on trial.

6) The court process is an adversarial/hierarchical system that gives attention to reasoned arguments and legal wrangling. It can be likened to a game with each party competing to win, except that one side (the defense) is given the advantage.

7) The formality and ritual of the courtroom can be intimidating. Respect is to be shown to the judge and order is to be maintained at all times. Observers are expected to remain silent and without emotion even when shaken by the proceedings.

8) Our system upholds the independence of the judiciary from the influence of elected officials. However, judicial appointments, new legislation and government policies reflect the political values and priorities of the government in power.

9) The effects of crime are long-term. Most victim services are designed to support crime victims in the short term.

10) Victims of crime need to take responsibility for their own healing and recovery. It helps to have the support of family and friends, and to know persons who understand the effects of trauma, crime and victimization.

11) For the most part, crime victims need to rely on their own resources to learn how the system works and to connect with resource and support networks.

12) Victims need to share their stories and find innovative ways of doing that without adding to their own trauma or the vicarious traumatization of innocent bystanders.

13) Victims of crime and their advocates are the ones who can best raise awareness and advocate for change in how the system views and treats victims. Most other folk don't understand the issues.

Hazel Magnussen
December 2004

Appendix III:

LETTER TO: Honorable Anne McLellan, Minister of Justice, Government of Canada

Honorable David Hancock, Minister of Justice, Province of Alberta

October 19, 2000

I am writing in regards to the recent Alberta trial in which Abraham Cooper was convicted of manslaughter of my brother, Dr. Doug Snider. My purpose in writing is to draw attention to the inconsistencies in the legal process that resulted in the lesser conviction of manslaughter and a sentence of only ten years less thirty-two months.

I understand that the law protects the rights of the accused by not allowing character evidence that might prejudice the jury. It appears that the accused and his defence lawyer abused that right and privilege using the legal system to denigrate my brother's character. After all, the defence didn't need to substantiate its accusations, didn't need to prove anything but merely needed to plant seeds of doubt. Cooper of course had the right to remain silent and not speak for his actions.

There was already strong evidence that my brother had been assassinated at the hand of Abe Cooper. Then, my brother, Doug Snider, not Cooper, was put on trial. The trial became a forum for the character assassination of my brother through bizarre, brutal and unfounded accusations and attacks. The position of the defence was more about how Abe Cooper sees the world and says much more about his character than that of my brother.

Doug Snider was a man of integrity and compassion who, although he had his human frailties, worked and advocated relentlessly for quality health care for his community. He would not willingly have given in to Cooper's demands. He would sooner have died.

The Crown was not allowed to enter evidence regarding Cooper's defiant behavior, his vindictiveness or his state of mind that motivated and enabled him to kill. Yet, in sentencing Cooper, Court of Queen's Bench Justice Joanne Veit noted that while Cooper was characterized as not accepting the decisions of others, 'it would not be fair to characterize him as aggressive or assaultive.' Did she not have access to the myriad of documents already on file? Did she not hear the distortion in Abe Cooper's thinking? Could the court not see his dangerous pattern of vindictiveness, projection of blame and counter-attacks of others? Did the court not recognize the vindictive language of a man who (in the words of the Crown) 'nursed his grievances,' hanging on to his 'cherished beliefs' that there was a conspiracy against him?

Could the court not see that this is a man who has consistently refused to be accountable for his actions, now shows absolutely no remorse for his crime and is likely to continue to intimidate and put others at risk? Did the court not know about Cooper's approach to the family after the defence's closing argument?

The letter of the law took precedence over common sense even in the final statement of the sentencing. Cooper, after release from prison, is not to have in his possession any firearms for one year. I heard no mention of scalpels, knives or blades of any kind – a surgeon's tools that were likely used to kill my brother.

Clearly, there is something wrong with this picture. I did not expect expressions of condolences from the justice system but I did expect truth and justice. What I experienced is not in keeping with my view or expectations of a civilized, just society. I did not expect that the system would condone further attacks on the victim nor further traumatization of the victim's family. All this occurred while the court ensured the proper interpretation of law and the protection of the rights of the accused.

Did the court turn a blind eye or just fail to recognize that Abe Cooper's character was a primary factor in this case. I waited, in vain, for a call for a mental health assessment of this man. Historically, his manipulative, at times charming and at other times intimidating behavior has been baffling yet entertaining for some but demoralizing and downright threatening for others. On May 5, 1999, it was deadly for my brother.

The Abe Cooper trial is an example of how our justice system is failing the people of Canada. The scale is tipped so far in the favor of the accused that public confidence in the system is eroded. The safety of the public and the rights of common folk who play fair and are trying to live their lives with integrity and respect for others are being sacrificed for the rights of criminals. I call for a review of the Cooper trial and an examination of the laws of our land that made this travesty of justice possible.

I ask the question: "Who is the law supposed to protect?"

Yours truly,
Hazel Magnussen

Appendix IV:

Recommendations for Regulatory Reform

presented by Hazel Magnussen at meeting of
the Federation of Medical Regulatory Authorities of Canada, June 2004

In a paper telling this story at the Physician Health Conference in Vancouver in 2002, I appealed for reform in the manner in which medical regulatory authorities deal with disruptive physicians. I conclude with a revised version of those recommendations:

1) Acknowledge the problem and hold physicians professionally accountable for their conduct. The CMA Code of Ethics includes the physician's responsibility to avoid impugning the reputation of colleagues, to collaborate with other physicians and health professionals and to seek help for personal problems that adversely affect their service.

2) Implement protocols for identifying, assessing, monitoring, treating and, when appropriate, disciplining disruptive behavior. (The Ontario Physician Health Program has already developed such protocols.)

3) Law reform to strengthen the authority of regulatory bodies to fulfill their mandate in ensuring safe, ethical, competent practice.

4) Screen patterns of disruptive and abusive behavior that threaten staff and patient safety.

5) Ensure that records of a physician's unprofessional conduct are forwarded to regulatory authorities when a physician changes jurisdictions.

6) Provide resources and support in conflict resolution as an alternative to litigation.

7) Provide support and protection for those who are targets of physical and verbal threats, false accusations and unfounded lawsuits.

8) Ensure accessibility to assessment and treatment programs specializing in disruptive behavior.

9) Raise awareness by offering health professionals educational programs about disruptive behavior.

10) Increase transparency in the complaint and disciplinary process.

Profile of the Author

Hazel Joan (Schattschneider) Magnussen, a graduate of the University of Alberta, is a retired registered nurse with 35 years experience in health care. The primary clinical focus in the last ten years of her career was mental health nursing.

Conscious of the moral issues and ethical questions that nurses and other health professionals face in their daily practice, Hazel undertook further study in theology and ethics at St. Stephen's Theological College in Edmonton, Alberta in the 1980s. Her articles regarding nursing ethics and nurse-physician relationships have been published in professional journals.

Hazel Magnussen

Since her brother's death, Hazel has written articles and presented papers on bullying and disruptive behavior in the workplace, and the experience and needs of victims of crime in the criminal justice process.

Hazel lives on the British Columbia coast with her husband, Lloyd.